FIRST STEPS IN

YEAST CULTURE
part one

by Pierre Rajotte

alliage
ÉDITEUR

PUBLISHED BY
Alliage Éditeur
30, Palmerston ave.
Montreal, QC. H3P 1V2 Canada
(514) 739-9424 • FAX (514) 739-2717
lupico@sympatico.ca

First printing - March 1994 / Second printing - February 2000

Design direction by Lucille Richard
Cover design by Hélène Deschênes
Illustrations by Hélène Deschênes
Photography by Luc Sénécal
Text editing by Janet Warne
Copyright © Pierre Rajotte, 1994
All rights reserved
Manufactured in Canada

Canadian Cataloguing in Publication Data

Rajotte, Pierre, 1939-
First Steps in Yeast Culture: volume 1

Includes bibliographical references

ISBN 2–921327–16–3 (set)
ISBN 2-921327-17–1 (vol. 1)

1. Yeasts. 2. Microbiology— Technique
3 Brewing
I Title

Legal deposit, second quarter, 1994
Bibliothèque nationale du Québec

TABLE OF CONTENTS

CHAPTER I: EQUIPMENT

Guiding principles 1.1, The inoculating needle 1.1, Sterilization 1.2,
Different flame sources 1.3, Flasks, recipients and test tubes 1.4,
Petri dishes 1.5, Pipettes 1.5, Alcohol 1.6,
Assortment of pots and pans 1.6, Pressure cooker 1.6,
What we will do 1.6

CHAPTER II: STERILIZATION TECHNIQUES

An overview of sterilization techniques 2.1, Heat sterilization 2.1,
Dry heat sterilization 2.2, Notes on dry heat sterilization 2.2,
Wet heat sterilization 2.3, Notes on Tyndallization 2.4,
An alternative to sterilization under pressure 2.5, Notes on spores 2.5,
Sterilization under pressure 2.6, Notes on pressure cookers 2.8,
Subsequent handling of sterile jars and flasks 2.8, Notes on alcohol 2.9,
References 2.10

CHAPTER III: WORT

CHAPTER IV: SOLID MEDIA

CHAPTER V: STERILE LOOP TRANSFER

CHAPTER VI: FIRST FERMENTATION

CHAPTER VII: STERILE TRANSFER: LIQUID

CHAPTER VIII: POURING PLATES

CHAPTER IX: PLATING A YEAST SUSPENSION

CHAPTER X: DILUTION

CHAPTER XI: THE POUR PLATE METHOD

CHAPTER XII: CLEANING GLASSWARE

Acknowledgement

This book is now a reality only because I had the opportunity to work with six extraordinary people, who I would like to thank here. They have all given me solid support right from the start.

The fact that I live in Montreal is very important, but more because Joris Van Gheluwe also lives here. Now retired, he was for many years the technical director of one of the major Canadian breweries. Known as "George" by his fellow members of The Master Brewers Association of the Americas, he is probably the most persistent and thorough private collector of brewing literature in North America.

His collection of scientific material in the fields of brewing and chemistry includes a few original books more than two centuries old, many a century old, and the great majority from this century. Most of this invaluable material is written in languages other than English. He graciously offered me unlimited access to his references. On many occasions, he was also instrumental in obtaining more recent material that was not immediately available. His relentless search for information in his vast collection of books, scientific papers, and various private communications made this book possible. He also accepted to review the complete manuscript, for which I am most thankful.

Antoine Khoury of the microbiological department of the Institut de technologie agro-alimentaire de Saint-Hyacinthe was the first person to show me the proper technique of microbiological manipulations and media preparation. He was also instrumental in obtaining the various media and ingredients needed for more advanced work. Today, more than six years after our first meeting, he is still more than eager to supply information on both methods and ingredients. He patiently reviewed the manuscript to ensure that the facts and methods were properly explained and technically correct.

Jérôme Denys of Le Cheval Blanc, the first Montreal brew pub, was faced with quality problems soon after opening. His problems were mostly caused by yeast of dubious quality. His keen desire to sell a product of superior quality quickly led him to take corrective measures. He made the necessary arrangements that enabled both of us to learn proper microbiological techniques, and did not spare any expense in acquiring all the basic instruments required to monitor the quality of his beer.

Alain Fisette and Jean Pierre Leblanc of "Les Promotions Zig-Zag", agents of European breweries, were instrumental in opening the doors to many breweries and brewing institutions in Europe. In their company, I had the pleasure of visiting breweries in most European countries, from Denmark to the Czech Republic.

Finally, I would like to thank Lucille, my faithful companion. A few years ago, she left a secure teaching job to embark in the exciting world of publishing. In a very short time she was producing best sellers in fields as varied as, theater, games and modern teaching material. I foresaw that one day she could publish brewing material of a scientific nature. She patiently coached me in the fine art of manuscript preparation, and this first volume is the result of her talent and patience.

Finally my thanks to the Carlsberg brewery for allowing me to visit the old brewery and the Hansen laboratory, as well as the Carlsberg Laboratory and its library.

ABOUT THE AUTHOR

Pierre has lived most of his life in Montreal. In 1963, he obtained a degree in mechanical engineering from l'École Polytechnique. Following graduation, he worked as an engineer for the Ford Motor Company in Dearborn, Michigan. After a few years he returned to Montreal, where he was employed as an engineer by a snowmobile manufacturer. In 1969, he realized a lifelong dream of self employment by starting, with friends, a snowmobile manufacturing company. From then on, he never looked back. For many years, he was engaged in various fields of motor vehicle engineering and sales.

In 1980, he undertook homebrewing. This remained a casual hobby until 1983. At that time, he was given a generous amount of both top and bottom fermenting yeasts used by a major Canadian brewer. The yeast gave his beer such a marked increase in quality, that it made him take up the brewing hobby more seriously. He came to the conclusion that yeast was really the "secret ingredient" of brewing, and resolved to learn everything he could about this fascinating subject.

In 1985, he spent a year in Paraguay working on a World Bank contract. Upon his return, he embarked in the brewing field on a full-time basis. He began by reading every book written on the subject that he could lay his hands on. At the same time, he also started his own brewer's yeast collection as an outcome of numerous trips to Europe. Every time Pierre was shown a new technique for handling microorganisms, he relentlessly practiced it until he could accomplish it with the same dexterity as the person who had showed it to him.

Already fluent in French, English and Spanish, Pierre undertook the study of German in order to tap the enormous amount of brewing literature written in that language.

In 1989, he introduced a one-barrel brewing system to the North American brewing community. Subsequently, he introduced breweries of two and four-barrel capacity. Since then, he has installed more than a dozen commercial breweries, spread out from Bar Harbor, Maine, on the Atlantic, to Nanaimo, British Columbia, on the Pacific.

In 1992, his first major book "Belgian Ale" was published by Brewers Publications in Boulder Co.

Although the majority of his customers had brewing experience, he quickly found that they all lacked the basic knowledge of proper yeast handling. The original goal of writing this publication was to provide a service to his customers. The complexity of preparing a complete yeast culture manual soon made him realize that he had to work very closely, almost full-time, with the publisher. To help bring about this publication, he had to acquire new skills in publication software products.

With this first volume completed, Pierre has already embarked upon the preparation of the second volume. Concurrently, he is setting up more new breweries throughout North America.

Introduction

Everybody can make beer, but not everybody can succeed at making excellent beer on a consistent basis. The reason behind this is quite simple. Many home brewers and even brew pubs and micro brewers are lacking the basic scientific knowledge required to brew and handle beer properly. This is very prevalent in North America, where anyone can make beer at home and anyone with a reputable background can open a commercial brewery. In contrast, other countries require that a commercial brewery operator acquire formal training in brewing science.

Although general information on beer brewing is readily available, some fields are less widely covered. The area where this deficiency is most evident is in the domain of yeast culture and handling. Numerous authors have scared people away from this field by making it appear as something impossible to accomplish successfully.

Brewing has often been called a combination of art and science. This is very true, but quite often brewers have developed the artistic side more than the scientific side. I consider the artistic side of brewing as being the talent of craft brewers to come up with a combination of ingredients and processes that create individual brews of a unique and superior quality. I truly believe that this creativity is something that you are either born with or have acquired and perfected through an excellent general education. Great brewers, like great chefs or great artists, have it in themselves to surpass others in the field of creativity.

However, creating a good recipe once is not the only facet of brewing. One must be able to repeat it and also improve upon it. This is where the scientific part comes into play. Understanding the principle behind every move that we make is essential to progress.

There is also a third facet to brewing that I consider essential, but which is never mentioned. I call it dexterity. It consists in acquiring skills for carrying out various manual operations in the correct and proper manner. This could be as straightforward and as important as having a simple, complete and thorough cleaning and sanitizing routine. Here again, this is for some people a natural talent. Others need to have the routine broken down and explained in order to repeat it consistently.

Of all the facets of brewing where skill and dexterity are required, proper yeast handling has been completely neglected. Many writers have discussed at length the various scientific aspects of yeast behavior, performance, and requirements. Yet very few ever mention or describe the simple and proper day to day operations that have to be performed.

Ten years ago I was given live brewers' yeast. It came from a major Canadian brewer. I was so impressed with the results, that from then on I was determined never to use anything else. At that time the only yeast available was dried yeast sold in small packets. Most of the time this dried yeast was bread yeast.

There is a big gap, however, between fermenting a brew once with live yeast poured from the jar, and doing it all the time consistently with your own cultured yeast. Although my first results with live yeast were crowned with success, I was still very far from being skilled in yeast handling. My second call for live yeast from the same brewer came with a stern remark: " *I am giving you yeast for the last time. Never ask me again. From now on you will have to take care of it yourself.*"

These remarks made a deep impression. I knew from the results that using live brewer's yeast was the only way to go, but taking care of it myself was far from simple. The only knowledge I had came from various articles in amateur brewing magazines. The authors would resume in a few pages various summary manipulations, but always with a severe warning that they were impossible to do at home or in a brewery without having recourse to a skilled microbiologist and sophisticated equipment.

Ignoring this warning I set about, with whatever was available at the time, performing some of the basic manipulations with varying degrees of success. Great beers were at times followed by disasters, but the rewards more than compensated for the failures. At least I was acquiring skill and some dexterity. The abundant "scare literature" by authors more skilled in reporting the failures of others than in describing proper procedures did not phase me anymore. After all, yeast does not bite back. The worst that can happen is an inferior brew. This you can live with, when you brew beer for only yourself. When you start making it for a living, however, you definitely have to look at it in another perspective.

In 1987 a friend of mine, Jérôme Denys, opened the first brew pub in Montreal, "Le Cheval Blanc". The various suppliers at the time made it quite clear that brewing beer was very simple. The only thing required was equipment. Just boil water, add malt extract, boil for an hour, cool and dump in the yeast. Ferment, filter and serve. And you know what, this is true. However, what do you do if the beer does not ferment completely, or worse does not ferment at all? Some brewers will sell it. Those who are more conscientious will dump it. This is where it can hurt.

After many dumping sessions, Jérôme and I finally saw a ray of hope when we were given the opportunity to acquire basic skills in microbiology. The Institut de technologie agro-alimentaire de Saint-Hyacinthe is a world renowned center for training in the field of food preparation. Students from all over the world come to the Institut to acquire basic technical skills in all fields of food production. Every aspect is taught, from planting the seed in the ground to raising animals and preparing food for human consumption. Of course, not every one learns all these skills, and there are several specialties. One of these is microbiology. In a completely equipped laboratory students can learn the various skills appropriate to microbiological applications.

Another of the Institut's functions is to help various industries engaged in food processing by providing training in particular skills. It was under this program that I was able to learn the basic operations necessary for proper yeast handling. Practical ways of performing the basic manipulations were heavily stressed. All these operations could be performed by anyone equipped with simple materials. The accent was truly on being practical: doing basic operations relevant to the food industry but using only basic equipment. The operations shown were not specific to brewing but of a general nature.

After completing this course, everything seemed more simple. Making the connection between the general food industry and brewing took a bit more time. Finding the various media and adapting the numerous techniques required much research in literature about the field of brewing. One thing was very clear throughout this search. There was no single book or publication in any language that simply demonstrated and described these basic skills. After many years, the numerous simple operations and tools required are presented here in an illustrated form never before published.

This should not be regarded as the end. The only thing that will make you skilled is practice. Here again, the important thing is to do the operations, and not wait for the ideal conditions to perform them.

Music is made from just eight notes. Some world renowned musicians work with very few notes, but they are good at it. They have acquired their skill through practice. Many of them start with very basic, sometimes cheap instruments. The skill they acquire is more a result of determination and practice than sophisticated equipment. The same is true in the field of yeast handling. Well performed basic manipulations, good simple basic tools, practice and learning from others more knowledgeable is all it takes. Leave the "scare literature" behind and refine your skills. You will be amply rewarded and satisfied.

I have written this book in such a way that it can be useful to either a person who has never manipulated yeast before, or to someone who already has a good knowledge of the subject. Beginners will benefit by reading the book at least once from start to finish. Then they should start practicing the manipulations that they can do with the equipment and tools already in their possession. People already skilled in the techniques of sterile manipulations can go directly to any chapter that describes elements with which they might be less familiar. In each chapter, they will find practical details that they can immediately apply.

The book begins with a survey of the methods and tools required. The techniques are then described in detail in successive chapters. First, I present the essential technique of sterilization, followed by its application in the preparation of both liquid and solid media. Subsequently, the preparation of plates and slants is fully described.

The manipulations themselves are presented next. These include the inoculation of sterile wort using the sterile manipulation techniques, followed by different methods of plating yeast. These methods are applicable to either yeast selection or yeast counting. Then I discuss the proper way of making a dilution, along with its applications. A brief overview of selecting and saving yeast colonies is also presented.

Finally, I present a step-by-step method of yeast propagation, applying all the techniques previously described. The forgotten century-old method of saving yeast cultures in a sugar solution is fully disclosed for the first time. A final section on yeast saving completes the first volume of this collection.

To simplify the reading, the metric system of measurement has been used throughout this book. A conversion table is provided at the end of the book for those who are not familiar with this system. Many of the items used in yeast cultures, such as test tubes, pipettes and petri dishes are made in metric sizes only. In addition, I know of no scale calibrated in ounces that is precise enough to accurately weigh the small quantities needed in the preparation of media.

Pierre Rajotte

FOREWORD

The world of yeast is the world of the very small. The unit of measure of this microscopic universe is called a micron. Its symbol is the Greek letter μ. A micron, or μ, is a length equal to one millionth of a meter. An average brewer's yeast cell measures 10μ in length and 7μ in breadth. If we made a column of yeast cells by placing them one on top of the other, we would need 100,000 cells to reach the height of one meter. This is a length just short of forty inches.

This book will show you the proper techniques needed to manipulate yeast cells. You will be able to take just one cell, and by giving it the necessary nutrients, obtain the required quantity necessary to ferment wort into beer. Centuries of accumulated brewing knowledge have shown that we must have, at the start of fermentation, a quantity of yeast equal to ten million cells per milliliter. If we were to measure the total length of all the cells that this represents, we would come up with a length of 100 meters. This is equivalent to the length of a football field.

Chapter I: **Equipment**

Guiding principles

All the manipulations taught in this book are those used by professionally trained microbiologists. However, if you have not had formal training in this field, you can perform all of these manipulations with success if you follow exactly the techniques described here.

The manipulations require basic tools such as: a burner, inoculating needle, various flasks and test tubes, pipettes and petri dishes.

You must also use sterile media. They can be either liquid or solid. The media used are of such a nature that anyone can either buy them or fabricate them to exactly the same specifications.

All operations must be executed in a sterile manner, that is, by flame sterilizing all the openings of flasks and test tubes.

So let's start by looking briefly at the different tools required, and how to use them.

The inoculating needle

The one tool that gets the most use is without a doubt the inoculating needle or loop. This basic tool is easily purchased. It can also be fabricated if you have the right wire. It consists of a handle onto which is attached a fine wire made, in most cases, from a nickel chrome steel alloy. It is abbreviated as a Ni Cr wire. The wire is usually terminated in the form of a loop, although some may end without a loop. It is held on the handle by a screw-on type device, similar to a drill chuck. The handle is covered with a plastic coating which gives a good hold, while providing good insulation. The handle should be held between the thumb and forefinger in a loose, comfortable manner, so that it is in balance.

STERILIZATION

Every time the loop is used it must be sterilized. Also available on the market are presterilized and individually wrapped inoculating needles made out of plastic. These throwaway types are at times useful when inoculating or collecting samples outside of the laboratory area. I personally prefer the permanent type, because the need to flame sterilize it prevents you from doing manipulations without having a flame source near at hand.

Flaming the inoculating loop

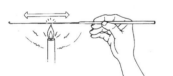

To sterilize the wire, put it in the flame until it gets red hot. Drag it through up to the handle. This way, any particles adhering to it will be calcined and rendered harmless. Before using it, let it cool down a few centimeters away from the flame. If you have to go deep into a flask, you should also flame sterilize the wire up to and including the gripping jaws.

Multiple benefits of the flame

Two benefits are derived from using flame sterilization. First, direct contact with the flame destroys bacteria, molds and spores that might be present on the needle or on the openings of various jars and flasks. Second, the flame heats the air immediately surrounding it. This heating results in an ascending air current in the immediate zone surrounding the flame. Therefore by working, opening, and closing jars in the immediate area of the flame, you get the additional protection that any airborne dust particles will be carried upwards by the hot air current. They are unlikely to fall into an opened container that is near a flame.

DIFFERENT FLAME SOURCES

Bunsen burner

What should you use as a flame source? There are many possibilities. In most laboratories a Bunsen burner is readily available. This type of burner can be fired with either propane or natural gas. It should be adjusted according to the type of fuel used. When properly adjusted, it gives a nice blue flame. The Bunsen burner produces a good quantity of heat, is readily available and is easily stored when not in use.

Alcohol burner

Another type of heat source that I also use quite often is the portable alcohol burner. This type of burner, such as the ones used in fondue kits, is quite advantageous because it can be used anywhere. It does not need to be tied to an external fuel source, and it is readily portable. It produces an appreciable amount of heat and flame, and will get an inoculating needle red hot as fast as a Bunsen burner can.

Solid alcohol burner

On occasion, I have used a solid combustible burner. This burner is very practical because it is all contained in one piece. It is both the burner and the fuel container. You only have to pop open the cover and light the fuel. It is ready for use. However, it does produce a flame over quite a large area. You must manipulate your tools and flasks according to this particular pattern. Its big advantage lies in the fact that it is available for use anywhere. It is easy to bring along when travelling, and does not emit any odor or drip liquids. However, it has a tendency to eventually dry out when not in use. So if you are relying on this heat source, check it out regularly to make sure there is enough fuel left in the can before preparing a transfer session.

Propane torches

Some people have used portable propane torches for flaming. They can be used, but personally I prefer an alcohol burner, which has a more gentle flaming action. However, propane torches are very practical to use when opening and closing a large stainless steel vessel used to propagate yeast in large quantities.

Other flame sources

People have been known to use the flame from a gas stove. I would imagine that in a bind this would work, but I believe that the flame is not adequately positioned to allow for comfortable manipulations.

FLASKS, CONTAINERS AND TEST TUBES

Test tubes

Glass tubes

A good supply of glass test tubes with screw-on caps must be on hand. Plastic presterilized tubes can also be used as a substitute. I definitely prefer the reusable glass tubes. All proper microbiological manipulation should always be performed with the help of flame sterilization. This is readily accomplished with glassware.

Plastic tubes

Presterilized plastic tubes do not need to be flame sterilized, and cannot be flame sterilized in any case. Someone who has a daily routine of opening and filling a lot of test tubes will save much time by not having to perform the flaming. Most people involved in doing yeast manipulations in a brewing environment do not do this on a continual basis. At times, you may do it every day, and at other times, once a week. In my opinion, it is better to use the routine of flaming every opening all the time. This can only be safely accomplished with glassware. Glass tubes are more expensive than plastic ones, but they can be reused indefinitely.

Test tube rack

For proper manipulation, an adequate test tube rack is recommended. Easy to find and very convenient is the utensil holder of an automatic dishwasher. It is very sturdy, can hold many tubes and has a nice carrying handle. The tubes and the rack can easily be stored away after use.

Flasks and vials

You will also need to have at your disposal containers or flasks of various sizes. There is no need to buy glass containers made for laboratory use. Recycled glass jars of various sizes can be reused very successfully and are an excellent substitute to lab ware. Their usage will be covered later.

PETRI DISHES

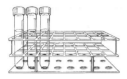

Another piece of equipment that you will require is the petri dish. This type of dish consists of two half dishes that fit one inside the other. The larger of the two usually has ridges inside it. This creates a small gap between the two halves to allow air movement. Formerly, petri dishes were made out of glass and had to be sterilized in the oven before using. These are still available, but I prefer those made of plastic and sold in presterilized form. Packaged in bags of twenty, they are very cheap, convenient, and ready to be used.

PIPETTES

The last item that is required to perform basic manipulation is the pipette. It is built much like a straw. It consists of a tube inscribed with graduating marks. The pipette permits you to measure a fixed amount of liquid. By suction, you can draw up liquid into it. Pipettes are made out of plastic or glass. They are purchased presterilized.

ALCOHOL

Alcohol at a 70% concentration is excellent for rubbing the surface of the working table and the exterior surface of glassware. It is commonly available in drugstores in the form of rubbing alcohol. It can also be used for rubbing your hands before starting microbiological manipulations.

ASSORTMENT OF POTS AND PANS

To complete the list of equipment needed, we should not forget a variety of pots and pans. Nowadays, those made of stainless steel are quite readily available at a reasonnable price. If at all possible, reserve some for your lab usage only. We will get to the aspect of cleaning these various pieces of equipment later on.

PRESSURE COOKER

Last but not least on the list is a household or restaurant type pressure cooker. The size used should be in relation to your need. For homebrewers, a domestic type cooker is sufficient. Micro and pub brewers will find the larger restaurant type cooker better for sterilizing larger yeast propagation vessels. Although not essential, its usage will save lots of time and always guarantees an excellent chance of success. Large laboratories use for sterilizing an apparatus called an autoclave. It works excatly like a domestic pressure cooker, but it's larger. Throughout the text, when the word autoclave is used, it can be substituted for pressure cooker.

WHAT WE WILL DO

With only these items you can perform many brewery microbiological manipulations quite adequately. You will be able to grow and preserve yeast strains and, with special media, isolate different strains one from the other, as well as yeast from bacteria. We will now see how to go about handling the media to obtain the desired results.

Chapter II: Sterilization techniques

The success of any microbiological manipulation is assured only when the materials, media and tools are sterile. When we speak of sterility, we mean that all form of life has been destroyed. This means there is a complete absence of either vegetative cells or their spores.

An overview of sterilization techniques

The major process used for sterilization is heating. There are other methods of sterilizing. One of them is sterile filtration. Another one is gamma ray irradiation. However, these methods require the usage of specialized apparatuses. These processes are more applicable to industrial concerns, who produce sterile equipment and supplies on a major scale. These apparatuses and processes are not necessary for general brewing microbiological testing and operations, and we will not go into them here.

Heat sterilization

Heat can be used in two forms: dry heat or wet (water vapor) heat. Dry heat can be either hot air, or heating over a flame. Hot air sterilization consists in keeping objects in contact with hot air at a certain temperature and for a certain period of time. Heating with the flame consists of either getting an object such as the inoculating needle red hot, or passing an object through the flame without getting it red, for example, flaming the opening of a test tube or jar.

Dry heat sterilization

First let's look at dry heat sterilization. This is normally accomplished in an oven by raising the temperature to 170°C and holding it there for at least 45 minutes. This means of achieving sterility is confined mostly to equipment that has to be kept dry, has a good stability at high temperatures, and conducts heat fairly well. In this category we find mostly glassware or larger containers that might be too big to fit in a domestic pressure cooker.

What is most resistant to dry heat?

In the world of bacteria, it is spores which are most resistant to dry heat. However, in the case of brewing microbiology this is not as relevant or important as in some other fields. Bacteria that shed spores are not encountered in finished beer, although they could grow in unfermented non-sterilized unhopped wort. Mold spores could be a problem, but only in cases of bad sanitation. As a rule, molds need oxygen to develop, and do not germinate under the presence of carbon dioxide. A typical example is the mold that can develop at the bottom of an empty beer bottle that has been put aside without rinsing.

What should be sterilized with dry heat?

I have on occasion used dry heat sterilization to sterilize large stock pots and various stainless steel funnels or apparatuses. Large containers need only be washed and closed, then put in the oven and left there for at least an hour. When they have cooled down, remove them from the oven and identify them as sterile. Open items such as funnels, paddles and so forth should be covered with aluminum foil. Simply discard the foil to use them.

Notes on dry heat sterilization

Authors of textbooks on microbiology do not always agree on the best temperature for dry heat sterilization. Following is a summary of their recommendations.

Source	Temp °C	Temp °F	Time (min)
A. J. Salle [1]	160 to 180	320 to 356	90
N. Marchal [2]	170 to 180	338 to 356	30
H. Birkenbeil [3]	160	320	180
	170	338	120
	180	356	30
C. Penn [4]	160	320	45
Collins and Lyne [5] (Figures recommended by the U.K. Dept. of Health)	160	320	45
	170	338	18
	180	356	7.5
	190	374	1.5
S. Lambin, A. Germain [6]	170	338	30

I have come to the following conclusion myself. It all depends what you are sterilizing. If you are sterilizing articles in stainless steel or glass, 170°C for 45 minutes should be quite sufficient. The only time you have to be more careful is when you sterilize articles which have cotton plugs such as pipettes. The cotton, which is white at the start, will acquire a cream color at 150°C. A bit further it will become more yellowish. When it has that color it has been properly sterilized. At a temperature of 180°C, it will form various tars which will make it a less efficient filtering media. It will also appear brown or even black.

This change in color can serve as a guide in calibrating your stove. Just place some pieces of cotton wool in the oven and adjust your temperature control to 160°C. After 45 minutes at this temperature, the cotton should appear cream to yellow. If needed, repeat this a few times to calibrate the temperature dial on your stove to the right temperature setting.

WET HEAT STERILIZATION

Heat in the form of water vapor is used either directly on objects such as test tubes and various glassware, or through convection on the liquids contained in such containers. The water vapor can either be at atmospheric pressure at 100 °C, or under pressure at a higher temperature.

Sterilization at atmospheric pressure

Water vapor at 100°C is the simplest form of wet heat sterilization that you can perform. It does not require any special apparatus. Everyone has the pots and pans necessary to accomplish this easily. Most microbiologists agree that the living forms of any microorganism are killed after being subjected to a temperature of 90°C for ten minutes. In the case of brewery bacteria, this takes place at an even lower temperature. Ten minutes at 75°C is considered effective in destroying beer spoilage organisms.

Notes on Tyndallization

Another method of sterilizing is also mentioned in many microbiological textbooks. It is named tyndallization in honor of John Tyndall (1820-1893), the British physicist who first proposed it. This method is still used today for sterilizing media that cannot support the high temperature of the autoclave. Blood samples and egg yolks emulsion are some times treated in this way. This method consists in submitting the liquid to be sterilized to heat, usually 100°C, and keeping it there for up to one hour.

This is normally accomplished by first dividing the liquid to be sterilized in suitable flasks and tubes, and then, by placing them in a rack. The rack is placed in a pan containing boiling water. With the pan covered, the water is boiled for at least fifteen minutes. The liquid is then cooled to at least 30°C. This heating and cooling is repeated every twenty-four hours during three days. The principle behind this is that by heating you first destroy the bacteria. If there are spore-shedding bacteria present, their spores will germinate during the cooling period. The subsequent heating will destroy the germinated spores. Doing this three days in a row ensures complete sterility. Most authors recommend that liquid subjected to such sterilization should be checked for bacterial development after the last heating. If no growth is noticed, then the liquid is considered sterile. This method is not commonly used in a brewery environment. It is only used in the sterilization of wort gelatine mixtures. It has been used in distilleries when they need to sterilize unhopped wort without resorting to the autoclave.

AN ALTERNATIVE TO STERILIZATION UNDER PRESSURE

When we sterilize wort to be used in culturing yeast we are concerned mostly with the destruction of wort bacteria, and the prevention of their appearance. Different sterilization methods can be used, depending on how the wort will ultimately be used. If you are going to use the wort immediately, a short 15-minute boil is sufficient to destroy all form of life. Give it a quick cooling, and the wort is ready for use. Practically speaking, this wort is sterile. If you are going to use it within a few days, this method is also applicable. The only variation is that we must package the wort better.

Notes on spores

Are spore-shedding bacteria encountered in brewing?

From a practical stand point, we do not come across spore-forming bacteria in the brewing environment. There have been a few isolated reports,[7] but these came from very specific cases that are normally not encountered. The only spore-forming bacteria likely to be found in a brewery would be a Bacillus. Researchers have reported instances of the growth of *Bacillus coagulans* in sweet wort. However, this Bacillus is hop sensitive and would be unable to grow in hopped wort and beer. On rare occasions, Bacillus has been reported in beer recovered from yeast. This beer is very different from the main fermentation beer. It has a higher pH and also contains many nutrients. This situation could only happen in countries where beer is taxed on the quantity and specific gravity of the wort produced before fermentation. Because the taxes on every drop of beer have been paid, brewers in such countries quite often recover all the beer from their spent yeast to blend with the rest of their beer. Few countries today tax their brewers in this way. This form of taxation is not used in North America.

Other situations of industrial yeast multiplication

Much of the practical information on brewing yeast and bacteria manipulations was written over half a century ago. At that time, yeast researchers were doing studies on the utilization of yeast in many fields. Some authors reported that spore-forming bacteria could be present in wort and nutrient media. The environment of yeast in a baking yeast factory or in a distillery is totally different from the one in a brewery. The propagation of baking yeast is accomplished by a mixture of molasses and various nutrients. No alcohol is produced. Distiller's yeast ferments the mash directly. Neither of these environments uses hopped wort. We sometimes forget that hops first came into use in the brewery because of their preservative qualities.

STERILIZATION UNDER PRESSURE

Although heating to 100°C will effectively destroy vegetative cells, moist heat under pressure is the most common method used to obtain absolute sterility. It is the only way to completely destroy bacteria and their spores. Spore destruction is complete only when a temperature of 121°C is attained and held for 15 minutes. Spores can resist destruction at 100°C for many hours. They also are resistant to dry heat. As mentioned before, spores are not a major danger to beer and wort. Sterilization under pressure is needed mainly to destroy the mold spores which can easily germinate on the surface of nutrient agar poured in petri dishes.

How is sterilization temperature reached?

Reaching the temperature of 121°C in an autoclave or pressure cooker is based on the following fact: pure steam under pressure (above the atmospheric pressure) will attain a higher temperature than the boiling point of water at atmospheric pressure.

It is very important to realize the meaning of pure steam. By this we mean only water vapor, and not a mixture of air and water vapor. If we have a mixture of both water vapor and air, the maximum temperature that can be reached is lower than with pure steam. Even if you read a pressure of 15 pounds per square inch, you will have a lower temperature, as the following table shows.

How to obtain pure steam

In a small domestic pressure cooker this means you should let the steam escape for a few minutes before setting the timer. For a larger type of pressure cooker, most manufacturers recommend that you let

Pressure gauge reading		Temperature with pure steam		Temperature with 66% pure steam	
Psi	Kg/cm²	°C	°F	°C	°F
5	0.35	109	228	100	212
10	0.70	115	240	109	228
15	1.05	121	250	115	240

steam escape for at least ten minutes before closing the valve. On units equipped with a pressure gauge, the timer should be set only when a pressure of 15 pounds or 1 atmosphere has been reached and has stabilized. At this pressure with the air fully expelled the temperature will rise to 121°C. It should be kept there for at least 15 minutes. When dealing with volumes of liquid larger than 500 ml, it is best to keep them at 121°C a bit longer.

How to cool down the pressure cooker

After the proper time has elapsed, you should turn down the heat source and let the unit cool before opening it. Contrary to common cooking practice, it is not recommended to force cool the pressure cooker. In cooking you do not want to overcook the food. In sterilization you cannot overdo it. Releasing the pressure prematurely can also be dangerous. This is very important when sterilizing a rather large quantity of liquid. The cooker itself might have cooled down, but the liquid inside the jar will still be superheated. A sudden opening could make it boil over, which could injure you.

How to arrange the items to be sterilized in the presure cooker

It is very important to realize that to be effective, the steam must be able to reach everything that is in the autoclave. There should be proper circulation of steam around the elements, and the caps should be loosely fitted. After cooling down they should be tightly screwed on.

Notes on pressure cooker.

An essential part of using an autoclave is to make sure that there is enough water at the bottom to supply the steam throughout the sterilization period. If at any time you sterilize equipment, glassware, or wort in succession, make sure between each session that there is always enough water. A good portion of it escapes as steam, and it is easy to miscalculate the quantity required. Top it up as required. If you ever run out of water, quickly remove the cooker from the heat source. In this situation, all closures and rubber parts should be discarded and replaced.

SUBSEQUENT HANDLING OF STERILE JARS AND FLASKS

Presterilized empty jars or bottles are a constant necessity in the brewery environment. They are useful primarily to collect samples in a standard manner, and they should always be kept in stock. You must properly identify empty sterile containers. When required for collecting samples, you will have no doubt as to their suitability. However, they should not be prepared too much in advance. Only brewers equipped with a proper laboratory have facilities to keep sterilized containers dust free.

Where to store sterilized objects

Brewery environments are quite notorious for creating turbulence in the air. The many fans and motors combined with the humid environment can create a haven for airborne particles. In many smaller operations, the laboratory equipment gets coated with dust. Wiping the outside surface of flasks and jars with a 70% ethanol solution before using them should be routine practice. This should also be done with any container that holds wort or liquid that may be used in the laboratory.

Although every small brewer would like to have an area set aside for doing laboratory work, sometimes they do not have the extra space available. In many cases it is better to perform some of these tasks at home.

What kind of jars should be used

Specialty glassware is nice and convenient, but recycled glass jars of any nature can be used. Any clean, heat resistant jar can be sterilized quite confidently. It is much better to have sterile bottles and flasks on hand ready to use, than to wait for the ideal vessel that may never come.

Notes on alcohol

Although not a sterilization procedure as such, wiping the outside surfaces of flasks, bottles, and test tubes, as well as the surface of the working table, is an essential part of a successful working routine.

Alcohol is an excellent germicide. Most microbiologists agree that it acts by denaturing proteins. This action is more pronounced in the presence of water. It has its maximum effect when mixed with water at a concentration of 70% by weight (77% per volume). In some areas it is possible to purchase drinking alcohol at a concentration of 90%. However, alcohol at this concentration has a lower germicidal effect than at a 70% concentration. Drinking alcohol, such as gin or vodka, is sold at a concentration of 40% by volume. Although good it is not as efficient as alcohol at 70%.

Alcohol at a 70% concentration is commonly sold as rubbing alcohol in drugstores. It can be either isopropyl or ethyl alcohol. Rubbing alcohol is always denatured with methanol to make it unsuitable for drinking. However, because it evaporates very quickly it can be used in all safety. It is excellent for rubbing the exterior surface of glassware and the surfaces of your work area. Some microbiology technicians routinely rub their hands with it before manipulations. It can also be sprayed on stainless steel components and set aflame for quick sterilizing.

REFERENCES

1. A. J. SALLE, *Fundamental Principles of Bacteriology*, 5th ed. McGraw Hill, New York (1961)

2. N. MARCHAL, *Initiation à la Microbiologie*, Technique et Vulgarisation, Paris, (1976)

3. H. BIRKENBEIL, *Einführung in die praktische Mikrobiologie*, Verlag Moritz Diesterweg GmbH & Co./Otto Salle Verlag GmbH & Co., Frankfurt am Main, (1983)

4. CHARLES PENN, *Handling Laboratory Microorganisms*, Open University Press, Buckingham, (1991)

5. C. H. COLLINS AND PATRICIA M. LYNE, *Microbiological Methods*, Butterworth Heinemann, Oxford, (1989)

6. S. LAMBIN, A. GERMAIN, *Précis de Microbiologie*, Masson & Cie. Paris, (1969)

7. McMURROUGH, I. AND PALMER, V., *J. Inst. Brew.*, 1979, **85**, 11.

Chapter III: WORT

Like all living things, yeast needs proper nutrients to be able to live and function properly. Much research has been done regarding the different nutrients and corresponding quantities required by yeast. Numerous artificial media have been proposed.

The addition of various salts and chemicals to regular beer wort has also been recommended. They have their merits. Many of these media are being used by researchers who are more concerned with yeast genetics and behavior under specific circumstances.

What liquid media is best for brewers?

This chapter will teach you how to prepare and save wort used for yeast propagation. To cultivate yeast and to multiply it for the purpose of fermentation, regular hopped beer wort is more than adequate. Properly made, it contains all the necessary ingredients and nutrients required by yeast in more than sufficient quantity. In fact, many microbiological media available commercially for the culture of not only yeast but also various microorganisms have beer wort as the major constituent. These artificial media are usually available in dry powdered form, and are quite convenient for use in laboratories outside of the brewing field. Since this book is concerned with brewing, we assume that the people who will most benefit from its methods and recommendations will have access to beer wort.

What type of wort is needed?

People who concern themselves with yeast manipulation in breweries always have numerous sources of wort at their disposal. Wort can be used unhopped from the mash vessel. At this stage it is easy to gather it at any specific gravity. It can also be taken hot from the brew kettle or even cooled from the wort chiller.

Try to obtain wort from a pale malt mash

At this stage there is one recommendation I can make. Preferably, wort that is going to be used for microbiological work should be made with pale malt only. This will ensure a consistency of basic raw material and eliminate the influence of unfermentables from the coloring malts. When collecting wort to be used for laboratory work, it is also suggested to gather a rather large quantity, at least 10 liters. Properly sterilized, it will give an excellent degree of consistency for any test you may perform.

Choosing a proper container

When gathering wort in a brewery any container is suitable, as long as it is heat resistant. It must also be a container that can be closed shut. I have used small plastic buckets with snap-on plastic lids very successfully. Because of the heat they become very flexible and soft. They have to be moved around with caution until the wort has cooled down. Of course, any wort kept this way should be adequately identified to make it easy for the user to know its origin and composition.

Preserving the wort

Once wort has been gathered, it has to be stored for future use. Depending on the end usage, two methods of conservation are recommended. For general usage it is advisable to sterilize the wort in the autoclave. If the wort is going to be used in the next few days, it can just be *"hot packed"*. This conservation method is just like home canning. It is fully explained further on in this chapter.

WHAT IS STERILIZATION?

The purpose of sterilization is to make sure that all living forms of any microorganism have been destroyed, and that all the spores of spore-producing microorganisms have been destroyed. Most microbiologists agree that all living organisms in a liquid are destroyed by submitting them to a heat of 90°C for a period of 10 minutes. On the other hand, spores which are produced by some kinds of microorganisms are more resistant to heat. They will only be destroyed when submitted to a wet heat of at least 121°C for at least 15 minutes. Fortunately for brewers, microorganisms that shed spores do not develop in beer. But some of them can become very active in wort, and even more so in unhopped wort. In the majority of cases, the spores that germinate are spores of molds. These usually require the presence of oxygen to manifest themselves.

WORT TREATMENT BEFORE STERILIZATION

When collecting wort for this purpose, take care to let it decant properly before submitting it to sterilization. This ensures that the least amount of foreign material will get carried over. A cold rest of 12 hours will result in a very clear wort. The majority of the heavier particles will fall to the bottom, and so will the cold break and its associated fine particles. The container holding the wort should be force cooled rapidly. When cooled to approximately 40°C, store it in a refrigerator or in a cold room.

Separating the wort from the trub

After decanting siphon the wort from the top, instead of pouring it out. This will ensure that only the clear portion of the wort gets carried over. Pouring will always rouse up the trub lying on the bottom. As an additional measure, the clear wort can be further filtered by letting it run through a cotton cloth placed in a funnel. This ensures that any remaining coarse stray particles are removed.

What happens to wort at sterilization temperature

The case of untreated wort

Let's look at how wort behaves itself when submitted to sterilization temperature. Wort that goes through sterilization always sheds a deposit, no matter how clear it was before you started. Wort that has not been submitted to Irish moss will be somewhat cloudy when it comes out of the autoclave. Wort that contains Irish moss will be clearer, but will contain more coarse particles in suspension. This creates no inconvenience except that the containers have to be set aside for a short while. The particles will eventually settle to the bottom.

The case of wort treated with Irish moss

Brewers who collect wort from the brew kettle at the end of boil and who also use Irish moss should note the following. The use of Irish moss in the kettle helps coagulate proteins, but it also results in a large accumulation of fine solid particles. Wort gathered from either the bottom of the kettle or the bottom of the whirlpool always contains many fine solid particles in suspension. Subsequent sterilization of such wort will result in a wort charged with loose flocculating particles. If you try to coarse filter the wort through a cotton cloth, before sterilization, the cloth tends to clog up quite fast with these fine, almost invisible particles. Through experience, I have found that a cold rest of 48 hours with wort containing Irish moss will result in very clear wort. After this amount of time, the very fine particles will have settled. Here again, the wort should be siphoned from the top instead of decanted. After sterilization such wort will become very clear but will contain coarse particles in suspension. They eventually settle.

How much wort should you sterilize?

It is a good practice to have at all times a good quantity of wort in stock. When you start working with yeast it becomes quite evident that wort is the commodity most in demand. We always seem to run out of it.

What kind of containers should be used for sterilizing wort?

Although laboratory quality glass vessels are recommended, they are not absolutely necessary. In my opinion, the end usage of the wort is more the determining factor than the vessel itself. I personally believe that you should try to use containers that fit in the specific autoclave that you have at your disposal.

The case of recycled glassware

The maximum size of the jar that can fit is more relevant than the type of jar itself. Mason jars are quite appropriate and readily available. I often use recycled glass juice jars of different sizes. Just fill them up and reuse the original screw-on lid. After you take them out of the autoclave they will make a popping sound when cooling down. This means that the lid is still good, and that the contents are vacuum sealed. If a lid ever becomes loose, just throw it away and use a new one. If you open a lid and hear no vacuum popping noise, don't worry. Just pour a bit of the wort in a glass, then smell and taste. Every brewer is able to tell if the wort is suitable for use. Even with lids that do not pop, I have yet to encounter bad wort when it has been sterilized in the autoclave. With large restaurant type pressure cookers, you can sterilize jars that hold up to two liters of wort.

Warm the glass before sterilization

One more word of advice. Although most recycled jars can withstand the high temperature of autoclaving, they should not be cold when placed in the autoclave, or filled with cold wort. It is always good practice to prewarm the jars and prewarm the wort to at least room temperature. Taking cold jars directly from the refrigerator to the autoclave will always result in broken jars, even when using high quality laboratory glassware.

How clear should the wort be after autoclaving?

As I have said before, wort that is submitted to the high temperatures of sterilization will always shed a deposit, no matter how clear it was to start with. Within a short while it will descend to the bottom of the container in which it was autoclaved. However, on occasion you may want at your disposal wort that is completely trub-free. Such a case is when you want to propagate new yeast from either a single cell or a slant.

How to get crystal clear sterile wort

Wort made from laboratory grade dried extract

There are three ways to obtain trub-free wort. First, you can start with laboratory grade dried prepared wort media. Most microbiological media supply firms offer it. This type of dried malt extract has been carefully prepared for lab usage, and when dissolved in water will give a wort that is trub-free. It is unhopped and is often used in laboratories engaged in microbiological work unrelated to breweries. For them it is quite convenient and practical. It is, however, expensive and unnecessary for brewers who have access to fresh wort all the time.

Wort made with malt extract

Of course, if you do fall short of presterilized wort and are in sudden need of wort, regular brewer's grade dried or liquid malt extract can be used. It must be pointed out, however, that when submitted to the high temperature of sterilization they will usually shed a greater amount of deposit than wort that has been submitted to the complete brewing and boiling process. One item needs to be considered regarding malt extract. Either dried or liquid, its composition is never known. Studies have shown that many manufacturers of extract also add sugars in various forms to their product. Therefore, if you want to use it as a media, you should use only one brand. This way you will have at least some degree of consistency, even if you are not sure about the actual composition.

Use only the top portion

A second way of obtaining very clear wort is to use only the top portion of the autoclaved wort, by decanting it carefully. When you need to fill test tubes with trub-free wort, this is the way to go. Just fill the tubes with this clear wort and resterilize them. They will not shed any deposit.

Filtering trub

A third way is also possible, but is practical only when you use lots of wort. Every time you use the top portion of a container of previously sterilized wort, keep all the trub deposit left over. Just accumulate it in a jar and keep it in the refrigerator. These trub deposits are already sterile. Although the jars have been opened, the wort will keep for a few weeks. When you have gathered about 500 ml of it, you will notice that the heavy portion of the trub has settled to the bottom. Gently pour the top portion over an ordinary filter cloth. This twice decanted wort will give you trub-free wort. Even the trub can be filtered out through the cotton. The accumulation of trub on the cloth will prevent any loose particles from flowing through. The trub drippings are also completely trub-free when submitted to autoclave temperature. When I need really trub-free wort, this is the way I prefer. Of course, after all this handling the wort has to be sterilized again.

The effect of temperature on wort color

One remark should be made regarding wort autoclaving. Every time wort is resubmitted to heat, it will acquire a darker color. Wort made from pale malt will acquire a nice amber color on the first autoclaving. If you submit it to another autoclaving, it will acquire a deeper color. This is one more reason why you should always use wort made from pale malt. After autoclaving, it could easily be assumed that it was made from an amber wort. If at times you fail to properly identify the composition of a wort container, a mix-up between pale and amber wort could result. Under ordinary circumstances this would not be of any consequence, but it could lead to a misinterpretation of results if,

in a fermentability comparison, pale and amber wort were
interchanged.

Notes on clarifying wort with egg white

Another age-old way of obtaining very clear, almost trub-free wort is to clarify
it with egg white. The addition of egg white to wort will coagulate most loose
particles. The white of one large egg is sufficient to help settle about two liters
of normal wort. To work properly, the wort should be at a temperature below
50°C. Separate the white from the yolk of a large egg. Slowly add the white to
the wort, mixing thoroughly all the time. Raise the heat slowly. As soon as the
heat goes up, your reaction will probably be "what did I do wrong?" At this
stage, the wort will look like milk. Keep on raising the temperature. Soon you
will see white flocs coagulating and the clarified wort will show through. **Do
not bring to a boil.** As soon as you can observe a good separation, remove
from heat. Filter everything through a cotton cloth. Sterilize the resulting wort
in the autoclave. It might leave a small deposit, but the resulting wort will be
brilliantly clear.

HOT PACKING

Although not a sterilization technique as such, I have successfully used
the following method of wort preservation for many years. First, you
must prepare the jars and containers ahead of time. Make sure that
they are spotlessly clean (as described in the section *Cleaning glassware*
in Chapter XII). Because you are going to fill them with boiling wort, it
is essential to warm them to the boiling temperature before filling. This
will prevent needless breakage.

Quick sterilization of jars

What I do is very simple. I use a hot water kettle, and bring a good
amount of water to a boil. Meanwhile, I rinse the containers and their
covers under hot running tap water until they get warm. When
thoroughly warmed up, I lay them on a table and fill them right to the

brim with boiling water. Then I cap them off immediately, and turn them upside down. Practically speaking, this has the double effect of getting both the cap and the jar in a sterile state. I let them sit like that for a few minutes. As soon as the wort has boiled for 15 minutes, I pour the water out of the jar, and pour the wort in.

Utensils needed

I have devised a few manipulations that greatly simplify the filling process, and ensure at the same time a great degree of sanitation. Some jars, such as Mason jars, are quite easy to fill. If you use a jar with a narrower opening, it gets more tricky. In this case you have to use a funnel. I strongly recommend that you get a funnel that will be used only for wort handling. They are cheap. So at the same time that I get the jars warmed up, I prepare another container of boiling water, in which I deposit the funnel, a ladle and a piece of wire terminated in the form of a hook. Preferably the wire should be made of stainless steel. There should be enough water in the container to cover all of these utensils. To do the manipulations safely, you also need a good pair of insulated rubber gloves.

MANIPULATION MADE EASIER

First, pour the water out of one glass container, and immediately place its cover in the container with the utensils in boiling water. Using the hooked wire, grab the funnel and put it in the mouth of the jar. If you are preparing a small quantity of wort, you can pour it directly in the funnel. If you have more than one liter, it is easier to use a ladle to fill up the jars. When the jar is filled, place the funnel and the ladle back in the boiling water, and retrieve the lid using the hook. Put the lid back on the filled jar, and go on to the next jar. When they are all filled with the required quantity of wort, let them cool. Once cooled, the jars should be stored in the refrigerator.

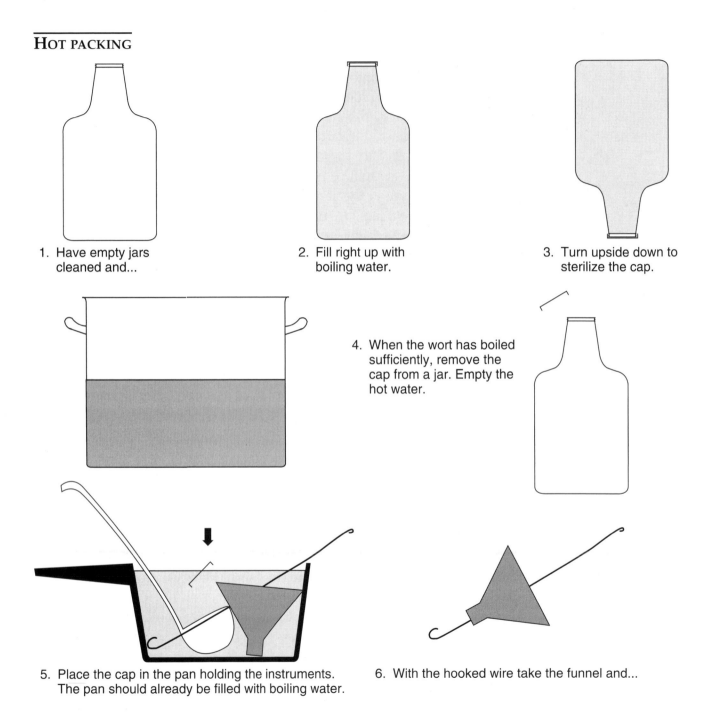

HOT PACKING

1. Have empty jars cleaned and...

2. Fill right up with boiling water.

3. Turn upside down to sterilize the cap.

4. When the wort has boiled sufficiently, remove the cap from a jar. Empty the hot water.

5. Place the cap in the pan holding the instruments. The pan should already be filled with boiling water.

6. With the hooked wire take the funnel and...

HOT PACKING

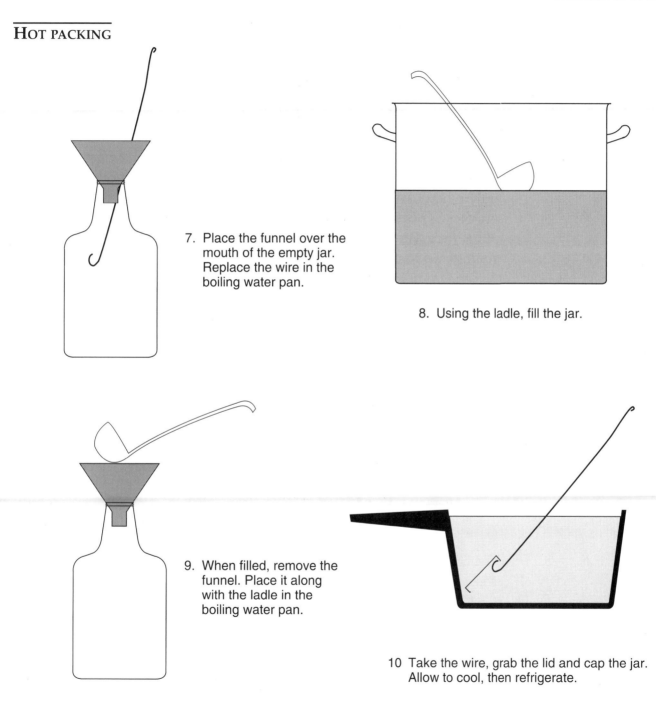

7. Place the funnel over the mouth of the empty jar. Replace the wire in the boiling water pan.

8. Using the ladle, fill the jar.

9. When filled, remove the funnel. Place it along with the ladle in the boiling water pan.

10 Take the wire, grab the lid and cap the jar. Allow to cool, then refrigerate.

3.11

HOW LONG CAN YOU KEEP WORT PRESERVED USING THIS METHOD?

I have used this method of stocking wort for over ten years. I have yet to see a wort go bad. There is only one drawback to this method. If you get involved with more than one yeast, and use quite a bit of wort, you soon run out of refrigerator space. It is also time consuming. I have kept a two-liter bottle of wort this way in the refrigerator for three years. When I finally used it, it still smelled and tasted as good as when it was first made. Nowadays I use this method of conservation only when I know that I will use the wort quickly. I find that it is quicker to put it through the autoclave. When sterilized in the autoclave, wort has the benefit of keeping indefinitely on the shelf at room temperature.

Chapter IV: **Solid media**

The need for solid media

Now that we have a good supply of sterile wort, we can go on with the preparation of the other necessary ingredients. Next to wort in liquid form, what is most needed is wort in solid form. It is essential for the preparation of plates for yeast selection and the preparation of slants for yeast collection.

The discovery of solid media

A century ago, when Pasteur did his first research on yeast and bacteria, he was using liquid media. The media he used varied from a simple infusion of hay in water, to wine must, beer wort and even artificial media that he formulated.

The first efforts

This worked fine, but was very limiting. In 1881, a great step forward was made when a young German medical doctor, Robert Koch, published a paper in which he described for the first time the usage of a solid media: the cut surface of a boiled potato. To accomplish this he used a sterile knife to cut a boiled potato in half. He did this under a large inverted glass jar in the form of a bell. Using the point of a needle, he spread the material to be analyzed on the cut surface. This spreading action separated the cells, and after a few days he could see colonies growing separately one from the other. Although this was a great step forward, it still left much to be desired. First of all, the large number of bells took up much valuable space in the laboratory. Because they often had to be lifted up and set back down, outside infections, mostly molds, would ruin experiments.

THE USE OF GELATIN

Koch was not only a trained medical practitioner, but also a photographer. In those days, being a photographer was not like today. You had to make your own photographic plates. Preparing plates involved coating glass plates with a mixture of silver salts and gelatin. Being a keen observer, Koch quickly realized that if he poured the gelatin mixed with some kind of bacterial nutrient broth on a glass plate, he would have a solid surface ready to use for spreading out the material that he wanted to culture.

The disadvantages of gelatin

This worked fine, but still had the disadvantage of taking lots of room in the laboratory. It also had another great disadvantage: gelatin melts above 37°C. Therefore, Koch could not incubate anything above that temperature. At that time, most microbiological research and discoveries were in the field of medicine. Because most pathogenic germs grow more easily above 37°C, there was a definite need to find a solid media that would be more stable at a higher temperature. However, this presented no particular inconvenience when working with yeast, because it grows very well at temperatures around 30°C.

The first experiments with wort gelatin

Emil Christian Hansen (1842-1909) is considered today as the founder of the modern fermentation technology. He came from a poor family. In his youth he was, like his father, an artist. After being rejected as a student at the Royal Academy of Arts, he studied to become a teacher. In 1876 he was awarded a Gold Medal by the University of Copenhagen for an original paper that he wrote on a "Danish fungus".

In 1877, he was appointed to a position at the Carlsberg brewery. His work consisted in observing the beer, on a daily basis, with a microscope. A year later he was appointed head of the Physiological Department of the Carlsberg Laboratory. His investigation of beer unfit for sale led him to the conclusion that the problem was not caused by bacterial infection, but rather by wild yeasts. He then tried to conceive a method of isolating the wild yeast from the good brewer's yeast. His experiments with single cell selection, were made using wort solidified with gelatin. At that time, buildings were not centrally heated like today. Laboratory environments were rather cool, so gelatin was not too inconvenient.

A substitute for gelatin

A solution to the inconvenience of gelatin was soon found. The wife of one of Koch's assistants, Frau Hess, had been using agar to help set her jam. A first try in the laboratory demonstrated its excellent qualities and suitability.

WHAT IS AGAR?

Agar is a substance that is extracted from a Japanese seaweed. It has very useful specific properties. Diluted in liquid, it must be heated to above 95°C before it will melt. When cooling down, it stays liquid until it reaches approximately 45°C. It has other qualities as well. It holds no nutrients, and does not contain any substance with inhibitory factors. If a committee of great minds had come together to invent an ideal substance, they could not have created a better one. Even today, more than a century after its first use, it is still the most commonly used solidifying agent.

The different grades of agar

Agar is readily available today. Several grades are sold. Companies that specialize in selling laboratory equipment and supplies all carry laboratory grade agar. The only problem with laboratory agar is that it is sold in quantities that represent more than a lifetime supply for home brewers and the majority of small commercial brewers. Many times I have used the type of agar sold in health food stores. Another convenient source is oriental markets. Although not as pure as the laboratory grade, it is available in small quantities at a reasonable price. Anyone who wants to try yeast culturing should not hesitate to use it. It will work fine, and will get you going successfully.

WORKING WITH GELATIN

Gelatin is still a viable means of solidifying wort, but it has one major disadvantage. Just like Jell-O, it remains solid only if is kept in the refrigerator. Yeast colonies growing on gelatin will eventually liquefy the immediate area surrounding the growing colonies. Brewers who might have difficulties in finding agar should not hesitate to use gelatin. After all, it is available in every supermarket. It is an excellent media to use, at least in getting started. However, you should be aware of its limitations.

The preparation of a sterile gelatin wort mixture is very different from that of an agar wort mixture. First, gelatin cannot be sterilized in the autoclave. The high temperature reached in the autoclave destroys its cells and renders the gelatin useless. It must be submitted to the process of tyndallisation to sterilize.

Prepare the gelatin mixture following the gelatin manufacturer's recommendations. Sprinkle it over the wort and let it soak. Wait a few minutes, then bring to a boil. Boil for 15 minutes. If you have used hopped wort, this in itself will prevent further growth of bacteria. The only problems likely to be encountered after the first boil would be the activation of mold spores.

Divide the gelatin mixture into flasks and tubes of various sizes. Wait until the gelatin is set, and then put it away for 24 hours. Then submit the flasks and tubes containing the gelatin to another 15-minute boiling period. Do this by placing the flasks and tubes in a suitable rack. Then place the rack in a pan half-filled with boiling water. Boil the water for fifteen minutes. Put the tubes and flasks away for 24 hours, and repeat the 15-minute boil again. At this stage, the gelatin should be sterile.

Some authors recommend using an egg white clarified wort (as described in the section *Notes on egg white* in Chapter III) when preparing a gelatine media. This is not essential. It depends mostly on the quality of the wort used.

WORKING WITH AGAR

The following procedure deals with the preparation of a wort agar mixture.

The ratio of agar to wort

The first step consists in mixing the agar with water in the right proportion suitable for yeast and general microbiological work. A ratio of 12 grams of agar in one liter of liquid will generally give excellent results. This will produce one liter of solidified liquid when set. Precision in weighing is very important. A good quality precision scale is a necessity. Adjustments may be required, depending on the source of the agar. Of course, even a one liter bottle of solid media is too much for any but a large laboratory.

The need for precise weighing

The preparation of wort agar mixtures requires precision in weighing and measuring. Anyone considering yeast culturing in a serious manner will need to acquire a precision scale or have access to one. A good laboratory scale that allows you to weigh hundredths of a gram is sufficient. Brand new scales are available for less than $200.00. Used ones can be found for much less. High precision analytical scales that are worth many thousands of dollars are not necessary for general usage.

Using a low-cost laboratory scale requires a few preliminary steps to ensure precision in weighing. The first step is to make sure that the scale is properly adjusted at the zero mark when empty. The next step consists in weighing the empty container into which you are going to deposit the substance to be weighed. When weighing dried substances such as agar or other media, you should never place it directly onto the scale. Rather, it should be placed onto an intermediate container. In the case of a powdery substance when only a few grams are to be weighed, a square 10 x 10 cm piece of ordinary aluminum foil is commonly used.

Place a small piece of aluminum foil on the scale and weigh it. Depending on its thickness, it will weigh less than one gram. Add the weight of the foil to the desired weight of the agar. This will give the total weight to be read on the scale. An expensive laboratory scale does not require this step. Just put the foil on it, press the adjust button, and the scale will read zero. Then add the substance to be weighed.

How much to prepare?

Small brewers will find it more convenient to prepare smaller quantities. Always keep in mind though, that any mixture containing agar should be autoclaved only once. Putting an agar wort mixture in the autoclave twice will result in a mushy and unsuitable media.

Measuring the liquid ingredients

Once you have weighed the agar, the next step is to measure the quantity of liquid. There are two ways to do this. If you have a graduated cylinder or any graduated measuring vessel, you can measure the volume directly. Another possibility is to weigh the liquid. Just weigh the empty container and add the weight of the liquid. When weighing, wort variations caused by different specific gravity will have to be considered. However, wort at 12°P 1.048 specific gravity can be assumed to weigh 100 grams per 100 ml. Exact precision is recommended, but in this case is not an absolute necessity.

Soaking the agar

When you have measured the required quantity of liquid, pour it in a container, and just sprinkle the agar over it. It is preferable to have the wort at room temperature. Let the agar soak in the liquid for a few minutes. Do not stir yet. Your eyes will tell you when it has absorbed enough liquid. When it is thoroughly wet, raise the heat slowly to dissolve it completely. Bring it to a boil carefully, and boil it for a few minutes.

Items to watch for

This is one operation that requires careful attention. A wort agar mixture is very prone to boiling over, especially when you have a lid on the container. To prevent this, use a pan with lots of headspace. I recommend using a pan that gives a 300% headspace. Although the quantity of liquid is small, boilover can be violent and can occur very suddenly. If ever a boilover occurs, it is best to discard the whole thing and start anew. The reason is simply that you probably have boiled overboard a greater proportion of agar particles than liquid. The resulting mixture will in most cases yield a solid media that is too soft to manipulate easily.

Divide the agar into small quantities

When the resulting mixture is completely homogeneous you are now ready to sterilize the agar. Just divide the liquid among several bottles or flasks. For the majority of small breweries or home brewers, the quantity of wort agar required at any given time is usually quite small. Therefore, it would be inappropriate to sterilize the agar in one big jar. It is much better to divide it into smaller bottles containing just the quantity of agar that will normally be used at any one time.

The right amount for your needs

Wort agar mixtures have two major uses. The first one consists in preparing slants for saving yeast. The second one is in the preparation of petri plates for more elaborate yeast work. Properly made slants will keep indefinitely. Petri plates are more fragile and have a very short shelf life. Plates are not sealed hermetically, and are in contact with the ambient air. Within a month they dry out. When that happens they are useless, and have to be thrown away.

The average small brewer does not need more than five plates at a time for routine work. Therefore, it is much more convenient to divide the wort agar mixture among smaller vials holding the right amount of media needed to prepare the number of plates required for immediate usage. Normally, a well poured petri plate contains 15 to 20 ml of wort agar. A flask of 100 ml is ample for pouring five plates. Remember also that the whole agar mixture has to be warmed up to 100°C to liquefy. This is accomplished much more quickly with a small volume than with a large volume.

Extending the shelf life

Some people go to the trouble of wrapping their plates with "parafilm" to extend their shelf life. This will work, but personally I find it easier to prepare the plates as they are required. It takes no more time to pour fresh plates than to wrap them up. When plates are freshly made, you can be sure of their quality and condition.

PREPARING SLANTS

Measuring the agar

The best way to handle hot agar for filling test tubes is with a pipette. Since the liquid wort agar mixture will be sterilized, you do not require a sterile pipette. As long as it is clean it is proper to use. A 10 ml pipette is the most convenient size for this work.

Pipetting

Simply draw approximately 10 ml of liquid into the pipette using your mouth. Plug the end with the index, hold horizontally and bring it to the test tube. Slowly open the end by sliding your index sideways and let the agar flow into the tube. The first time you do this, you will probably have to stop frequently and slant the test tube to check if you have enough agar. Pipetting is fully described and illustrated in the section *How to sterile transfer with a pipette,* Chapter x.

A well made slant

The agar slope on properly made slant begins approximately 4 cm below the test tube opening. After you have accomplished this a few times, you will know exactly how much to put in for a proper slant. The quantity depends on the size of the test tube that you are using.

What to prepare first

When dividing wort agar, start by filling the slant tubes when the mixture is still very hot. In the autoclave, the tubes must be in a vertical position. I place mine in regular household tin cans of various sizes.

What to use to close the flasks

Next, fill the individual 100 ml containers. Sterilization of these vials is slightly different. Formerly, all jars and tubes were closed with cotton plugs. Although this is still in usage today, I find it much more convenient to use polyplugs. These are small cylindrical stoppers made out of foam. They are very easy to remove and replace. They come in many sizes, and fit almost any size of mouth opening. The only drawback to them is that they are available only in very large quantities, usually by the thousand. They are cheap, but try to keep the inventory down. Try to standardize your glassware dimensions, so as to require only a few sizes.

SOLID MEDIA PREPARATION

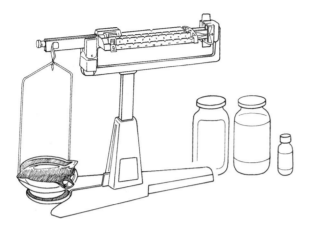

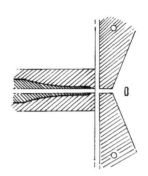

1. To weigh the ingredients use a good precision scale.

2. Before starting, make sure that the scale is adjusted to zero.

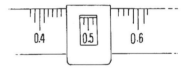

3. Place a small piece of aluminum foil measuring approximately 10 x10 cm on the scale and weigh it.

4. A piece this size will weigh approximately 0.5 g.

Precision in weighing is extremely important. When preparing 100 ml of wort agar, only 1.2 g of agar is required. This is a very small measurement for which only a precision scale is accurate enough.

SOLID MEDIA PREPARATION

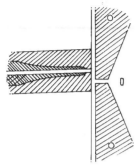 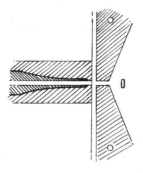 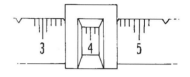

5. Be precise, and get the scale on exactly the zero mark.

6. When equilibrium is reached, note the exact weight of the foil.

7. Add the desired weight of agar to the weight of the foil to obtain the total reading.

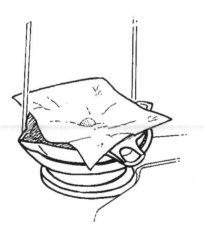 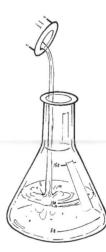

8. Use a spoon or spatula to place the exact quantity of dried agar on the scale.

9. Measure the required quantity of liquid using a graduated flask or tube.

STERILIZATION

Once you have filled the tubes and vials, you are ready to continue with the next step: sterilization of the wort agar. Test tubes holding the agar should be closed, but the caps should not be tight on the tubes. To be properly sterilized, steam must act both outside and inside.

Cover the openings with aluminum

As an additional precaution, it is a good practice to cap larger vials with aluminum foil before autoclaving. This will prevent dust accumulation during storage. When you need to use them, just throw the aluminum foil away.

Controlling the quantity

Because polyplugs are not air tight, the flask contents may dry out after a while. To control this, I just stick a short piece of masking tape on the cooled vials at the level of the liquid. After a while, if they dry up, you will notice that the level of the contents drops below the level of the tape.

Solid stoppers

A solid rubber stopper is another type of closure you can use. They are very convenient to remove and replace. Their solid feel makes manipulation easier for the beginner. However, a bit of caution is required. Because of the high pressure and temperature of sterilization, they will in most cases pop out of the mouth opening. To prevent this, a good trick is to insert a piece of ordinary cotton string between the rubber stopper and the vessel opening. This lets the extra pressure get out during sterilization. Rubber stoppers should also be covered with aluminum foil.

Cooling after sterilization

Once the proper time required for sterilization has elapsed, let the pressure cooker cool down naturally. Do not force cool it and most importantly, do not open it right away. When the autoclave has cooled down, remove the lid and take out the tubes and containers.

When material comes out of the autoclave, it is very very hot. Use extra care and caution. Have either a pair of insulated gloves or thick rubber gloves at your disposal.

Removing the pressure relief string

Remove the flasks that you have closed with solid closures, and holding the closure with one hand, pull out the pressure relief string with the other. The string that was dry when you first put it in is now wet and slippery. A gentle pull downward is all that is required to make it slip off easily.

Cooling the tubes for slants

After sterilization is complete remove the test tubes. Then tighten the closures and set them down at the proper angle to obtain a good slant. The agar should extend from the bottom of the tube to between 4 or 5 cm below the opening. They will set quickly, and are now ready to store for future use.

You will notice that condensation accumulates on the side walls of the tubes as they cool. This is normal. In fact, this small amount of sterile liquid will make it easier to spread yeast cells on the agar surface.

Storing the solid media

When the individual bottles of agar are set, they should be stored in a cool dust-free place. They will keep indefinitely if the work has been properly done, and the container closed with a solid closure.

Solid media preparation

10. Pour the measured volume in a suitable pan. The wort or liquid should be at room temperature.

11. Sprinkle the agar powder evenly over the liquid surface. Let the agar absorb moisture gradually for ten minutes.

12. Heat the agar wort mixture gradually. Stir occasionally to prevent lump formation. BE CAREFUL OF BOILOVER.

13. When the mixture has boiled for 5 minutes, divide it between your various flasks and test tubes.

SOLID MEDIA PREPARATION

14. The bottle on the left is closed with a foam type plug.
    The one in the middle has a solid rubber stopper and a pressure relief string.
    The bottle on the right has its closure covered with aluminum foil.

15. Put the required amount of water in the pressure cooker, and place the flasks inside. Their closures must be covered with aluminum foil. Sterilize for 15 minutes at 121°C.

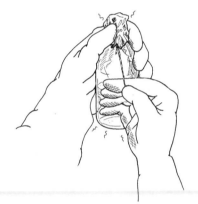

16. Let the pressure and temperature fall. When cooled sufficiently, remove the flasks and tubes using insulated rubber gloves.

17. Holding the aluminum foil and closure with one hand, pull on the pressure relief string. It will slip off easily.

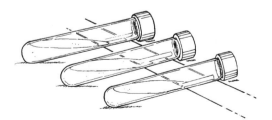

18. Place the slants at a proper angle for setting. When solidified, the agar surface should start 4 to 5 cm below the opening.

Chapter V: Sterile loop transfer

So far, we have discussed how to prepare the basic ingredients required for yeast manipulation. We will now proceed with the manipulation and handling techniques.

What is a sterile transfer?

A sterile or aseptic transfer is the transfer of a microorganism from one container to another container without picking up contamination from the environment. The container to which we are transfering the microorganism will in all cases be sterile, and contain sterile media. In this chapter, we will look at how to do such a sterile transfer using a flame sterilized inoculating loop.

Characteristics of the inoculating loop

The basic tool that is used to perform yeast manipulation is the inoculating loop. Commercial models of inoculating loops are sold by all scientific equipment suppliers who carry microbiological supplies. The inoculating loop consists of a handle, onto which is affixed a fine wire that terminates in the form of a loop. The handle is usually made of aluminum, is plastic coated, and has a screw type clamp at the end. This clamp, similar to a drill chuck, holds the wire in place.

The size and type of wire

The actual wire and inoculating loop can be made out of many materials. Selection of the material is based on the type of manipulation to be performed. For the purposes of yeast handling, loops made of an alloy of chrome, nickel and steel are very suitable. They are not very expensive and will last a long time. There is no need to use wire made of platinum. Although they last forever, their price does not warrant their usage. The wire and loop assembly should be between 70 and 100 mm long. A wire diameter of B & S 26 wire gauge is adequate. Wire of this size has a diameter of 0.016 in (0.5 mm).

Variants of inoculating loop

Loops with these specifications turn red hot very quickly in the flame and cool down very rapidly when removed. They are perfect for transferring liquid drops and picking solid samples from agar surfaces. Personally, I also like to use an inoculating loop made of a slightly larger diameter wire. Years ago, when I attempted my first yeast manipulations, I had no proper inoculating loop. I had to make one from scratch, and the only wire I could readily find was a piece of stainless steel wire with a diameter of 0.035 in (1mm). I mounted this on a drawing pen handle, and have used it ever since. Its main drawback is that it takes a bit more time to glow red, and requires a longer cooling down period. However, I find that it does give a better feel when spreading droplets on a petri dish or streaking a diluted yeast solution. This spreading or streaking technique will be discussed later on.

MANIPULATING THE LOOP

The handle of the inoculating loop holder should be balanced between your thumb and index finger. Depending on the type of transfer you will be performing, you start by getting the loop red hot. You then proceed all the way to the handle gripping jaws.

If you go into a deep flask

At times you will even flame the jaws if you have to go deep down into a large jar. This operation burns and destroys any material that might have adhered to the wire during previous manipulations. You may see ash particles clinging to the loop. You can shake them loose or even rub the loop on the Bunsen burner tube to dislodge them. Of course, after rubbing, the loop should be flamed again.

The zone of the flame

Once you have finished this, the loop should be drawn back, kept in an area between 5 to 6 cm away from the flame, and allowed to cool down. This area of approximately 6 cm in diameter surrounding the flame is considered sterile and is called the zone of the flame.

WHAT IS NEEDED TO PERFORM THIS OPERATION

- A flame source
- The inoculating loop
- A yeast slant in a glass test tube
- A glass test tube containing sterile wort
- A test tube rack

THE PROPER WAY OF DOING A STERILE TRANSFER WITH THE LOOP

Let's now look more closely at the proper technique that should be used when doing a sterile transfer. This type of transfer ensures complete sterility, if carried out with the proper equipment and procedure.

Let's assume that you have a slant, and that you want to inoculate a test tube containing sterile wort. A slant is a test tube holding a yeast sample spread out on sloped agar. Pure yeast cultures are often shipped in this form.

BREAKDOWN OF THE MANIPULATION

- First sterilize the wire loop, and let it cool down 5 to 6 centimeters away from the flame.
- Bring the tube to the palm of the hand holding the loop. Grasp the cap with the little finger. Unscrew the tube from the cap, and bring its opening in the flame. Twist the opening through the flame to burn any dust particles that might have adhered to the surface.
- Withdraw the tube from the flame. Keep the opening in the zone of the flame.
- Insert the cooled wire into the tube, and place it on the agar surface away from the yeast to let it cool. Wait a few second. With the looped end gently drag some yeast from the surface of the slant.
- Without touching the opening or the walls of the tube, withdraw the wire and keep the loop in the zone of the flame.
- Reflame the opening of the tube.
- Put the cap back on the tube.
- Set the test tube down in its rack.
- Pick up the other tube containing sterile wort.
- Repeat the opening and flaming operation.
- Insert the loop into the liquid and give it a brief twist or shake.
- Withdraw the wire.
- Flame the test tube opening and cap.
- Flame sterilize the wire and loop completely once again.

PICKING A YEAST SAMPLE WITH THE LOOP UNDER OTHER CONDITIONS

Sources of yeast samples are varied and numerous. They can range from a certified pure yeast culture to the yeast deposit at the bottom of a refermented beer bottle. Although the opening of the tube or bottle holding the yeast sample should be flame sterilized, there are containers made of plastic that simply cannot be passed through the flame.

What to do with a plastic container

Containers such as the bag, pouch, or plastic tubes which contain yeast cultures sold by some yeast suppliers obviously cannot be flamed. In such cases, the only solution is to draw the sample with a flame sterilized loop, and transfer it to either an agar surface or a sterile tube without flaming the opening of the container. This type of transfer is something we have to do quite often. It is a manipulation that must be performed with all the care you can take, but one step in the transfer technique is not according to good practice.

How good is a transfer without flaming?

This kind of transfer is as sterile as the material available, and will be adequate in the majority of cases. However, if you intend using the yeast in a commercial brewery, it always requires a further check later on to fully ascertain the quality and purity of the yeast. The various operations and tests that you can perform to ensure that the yeast is indeed a good yeast culture will be covered in the second volume of this book.

PRACTICE MAKES PERFECT

Although these operations are easy to perform, they do require a bit of practice. Keeping the wire loop within the zone of the flame when it holds either a drop of liquid or a dab of yeast is what most people have difficulty in mastering. You should hold the inoculating needle steadily in the right hand while your left hand is twisting and moving. Keeping the right hand steady while doing movements with the left hand is a bit like juggling. I have demonstrated and showed these simple manipulations to many people. Practice is essential for it to become second nature. This can be done with just water.

Sterile Transfer with the Inoculating Loop

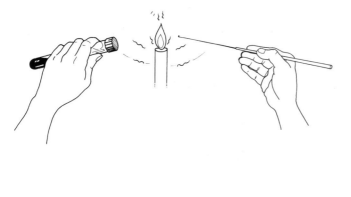

1. The tube in the left hand holds a slant. The flame is on. The inoculating loop is in the right hand.

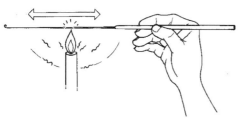

2. Starting at the tip, flame the inoculating loop all the way to the gripping jaws.

3. Keep the loop 5 to 6 cm away from the flame, and bring the tube to the palm of the right hand.

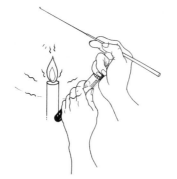

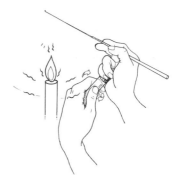

4. Grasp the cap with your little finger.

5. Unscrew the tube, by twisting the left hand.

Sterile transfer with the inoculating loop

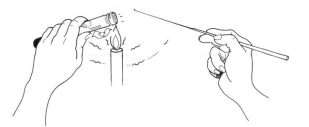

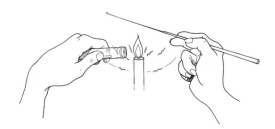

6. Holding the tube at a slight angle, bring it near the flame. Twist the tube all the way around in the flame. Keep the loop 5 to 6 cm away from the flame.

7. Withdraw the tube to about 5 or 6 cm away from the flame.

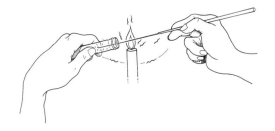

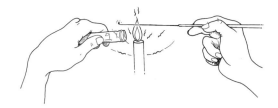

8. Plunge the wire inside the tube, and place it on the agar surface away from the yeast to let it cool. Wait a few seconds. With the looped end, gently drag some yeast from the surface of the slant.

9. Carefully withdraw the wire when some yeast is attached to the loop. Keep the loop approximately 5 to 6 cm away from the flame.

10. Twist and turn the tube in the flame again. Keep the loop approximately 5 to 6 cm from the flame.

11. Screw the tube back in its cap. All this time, keep the end of the loop 5 to 6 cm away from the flame.

STERILE TRANSFER WITH THE INOCULATING LOOP

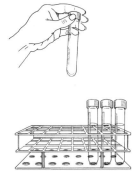

12. Place the slant in the test tube rack.

13. Take a test tube containing 10 ml of sterile pale malt wort.

14. Place the tube in the palm of the right hand, and with the little finger grasp the cap. Unscrew the tube and bring the opening to the flame.

15. Flame the mouth of the tube. During all these manipulations keep the loop holding the yeast particles 5 to 6 cm away from the flame.

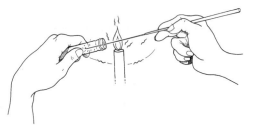

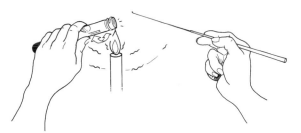

16. Without touching the opening or the walls of the tube, bring the loop inside the tube and plunge it in the wort. Give the loop a slight twisting motion to dislodge the yeast.

17. Withdraw the loop and...

5.8

STERILE TRANSFER WITH THE INOCULATING LOOP

18. Thoroughly flame the opening.

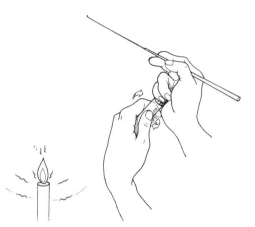

19. Bring the tube to the right hand and screw it on the cap.

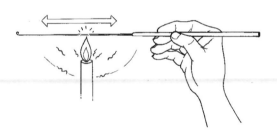

20. Flame sterilize the wire and loop completely once again.

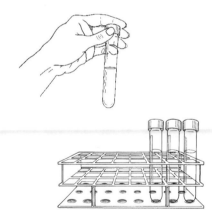

21. Place the inoculated tube in the test tube rack.

Chapter VI: **First fermentation**

Signs of fermentation

After inoculating the yeast cells in wort, you will not see any signs of activity for at least six hours. The first signs of fermentation will depend on the amount and the age of the yeast cells that were picked up. The yeast from a fresh slant or from a petri dish consists of mostly young and vigorous cells. In this case, expect to see signs of fermentation within six to twelve hours.

What about a slow start?

If the yeast came from either an old slant, the bottom of a bottle conditioned beer, or a diluted yeast sample, it might require twenty-four hours before showing signs of activity. Any inoculated tube that does not show signs of activity after twenty-four hours must be considered with caution. It will, under all circumstances, require further investigation and testing. Usually, you will have to plate out a dilute solution and pick out individual colonies for fermentation testing. This subject will be covered in Chapter XIII.

What should I look for?

The first observation you should make after inoculation, is to look at the level of turbidity of the wort. The greater the turbidity, the more cells you have picked up with the loop, and the sooner you should expect to see signs of fermentation.

The first sign of activity

After a few hours, you will observe a powdery deposit of trub at the bottom of the test tube. This is normal with wort. The visible start of fermentation is always accompanied by a lowering of the pH level. Although the wort in the tube is very clear, even after autoclaving this increase in acidity will result in a coagulation of wort proteins. Up to now, the proteins have been completely dissolved in the wort.

The second sign of activity

Very shortly afterward, a white flaky deposit appears at the bottom of the test tube and at times along the sidewalls. These are the first yeast cells of the new generation. The quantity of cells will increase substantially in the next few hours. At this stage, you should start to loosen up the cells from the glass tube.

RELEASING THE CO_2

Normally the cap of the test tube is tightly closed. When you loosen it up, you will hear a small release of pressure. **Always loosen the cap before moving the test tube around**. If you either twist, rotate or move

Releasing excess CO_2

Getting the yeast in suspension

the test tube too briskly before loosening the cap, fermenting wort might gush out of the tube upon loosening the cap.

What to do if wort gushes out?

If wort gushes out, it is better to discard the culture and start anew. Wort that seeps out of the tube can get in contact with dust particles outside of the tube. It can draw these particles back in by capillary action. In particular, this will happen if you are using a test tube that has not been wiped clean on the outside. When multiplying wort for fermentation, if gushing happens you should discard.

If you cannot check your fermentation tubes often, do not keep the cap screwed on tightly.

If you inoculate wort with yeast, and know you will not look at it for a day or more, like on a weekend, keep the cap cracked open. This way, the excess CO_2 can escape. Even so, precaution is required when manipulating the tube. There is quite a large amount of dissolved CO_2 and spillover is still a possibility.

How to release the excess CO_2?

To avoid gushing and spillover, twist the tube around or give it a circular movement to permit the gas to escape. Do not forget that test tubes are long cylindrical vessels. The surface of escape for the CO_2 is relatively small. Just remember what happens when you pour a well carbonated beer into a tall fluted glass. Expect the same result in a test tube.

How long does it take to release the CO_2?

Many factors have to be considered to determine the amount of time required. Generally speaking, if you release the CO_2 every six hours, five minutes at a time is sufficient. Doing it regularly is really the most important factor. When enough gas has escaped, start to move the tube around more vigorously to loosen up the yeast completely.

WHEN DO I TRANSFER TO A BIGGER TUBE?

Practically, yeast transfer from a small test tube to a larger one should be done no later than 24 hours after you observe the first signs of yeast deposit. Usually, I transfer yeast six hours after the first signs of CO_2. After 24 hours, the transfer becomes more time consuming. Quite a bit of dissolved CO_2 is present, and the yeast quantity is larger. Also, the yeast sticks quite tenaciously to the bottom.

When all the yeast is in suspension, prepare for transfer to a larger tube. Act quickly, because in 15 to 30 minutes it will have settled out anew.

Observing some yeast characteristics

Loosening up the yeast deposit allows you to observe a very important yeast characteristic. Yeasts that clump together are the flocculating varieties, while yeasts that loosen quickly are more powdery. Powdery yeasts normally take more time to settle down after fermentation.

Chapter VII: Sterile transfer: liquid

Once you have inoculated a test tube with yeast and it is actively fermenting, the next step is to transfer the fermenting liquid to a larger tube or flask under sterile conditions. This is a simple process, but you will require practice to become proficient.

What is required to do this operation

- The fermenting test tube.
- A large tube or flask that can hold three to four times the amount of wort contained in the fermenting test tube.
- A flame source.
- Rubbing alcohol and a clean, lint-free piece of tissue or cloth.

Getting prepared

First, wipe the outside surfaces of both tubes. For this, you can use a lint-free piece of tissue or cloth wetted with 70% rubbing alcohol. Although this operation is not essential in all circumstances, such as when you have just sterilized the larger tube in the autoclave, it is nevertheless a good practice to follow all the time. The reason for this is simple to understand. If you prepare test tubes ahead of time, they will accumulate minute particles of dust on the closure and on their outside surface. Sometimes you do not see them, but if you have month-old test tubes the dust will be quite evident. Wiping the tubes ensures that the dust is safely removed, and that any stray bacteria or mold gets a good soaking of alcohol. Subsequent flaming will take care of any particles that may still adhere to the surface.

Get the yeast completely in suspension

The following step consists in getting all the yeast in the fermenting tube in suspension, and most of the dissolved CO_2 released from the solution (described in the section *Releasing the CO_2* in Chapter VI). This operation must be started some time before you actually prepare to do the transfer.

Proceed in a comfortable manner

The transfer itself requires an equal amount of work from both hands. Although I will describe the operations the way I do it, it is quite acceptable to inverse the manipulations from the right to the left hand, if you wish. Do them whichever way you feel more comfortable. Although I am right-handed, I prefer to do the actual pouring with my left hand when performing this type of transfer.

THE TRANSFER, STEP BY STEP

The fermenting tube

To start the transfer, open the tube that holds the fermenting wort. Take the fermenting tube in your left hand, and place its cap in your right hand. With the little finger of your right hand, grab the cap and hold it between the little finger and the palm of your hand. With your left hand, partially unscrew the tube from the cap. Do this a few inches away from the flame. Unscrew it completely, and bring the opening to the flame. Rotate it with a twisting action and flame it thoroughly. Do not be afraid to get it hot. Meanwhile, your right hand is still holding the closure.

Details to watch for on the fermenting tube

Make sure you keep the opening of the cap facing down. After you empty the wort in the larger tube, you will not be using the first tube, but it is still a good practice to keep both the tube, and its cap sterile.

After pouring, a few drops always remain at the bottom. This is all you will need to perform an examination with the microscope. If, by inadvertence, some liquid falls on the outside threads of the tube, you will need to char them. The opening might look messy but it will be easy to clean afterwards.

The larger tube

When you begin to work with the second tube, you must be very careful to keep the opening of the first tube as close as possible to the flame. The first tube should be held at a slight angle, just enough to keep the liquid inside approximately 5 cm from the opening.

While keeping the opening of the first tube within the zone of the flame, use the little finger of your left hand to grab hold of the closure of the second larger tube. Twisting with your right hand, unscrew the tube from the closure. As soon as the cap is removed, bring the opening of the larger tube to the flame.

Details to watch for

At this stage, it is important to ensure that the closure of the second tube is facing down. It will be screwed back on the tube, so you must take every precaution to ensure that nothing falls in. Flame the second tube as you did the first one, always keeping the first tube near the flame. Only a few seconds are required to flame properly.

POURING THE LIQUID FROM ONE TUBE TO THE OTHER

Slowly withdraw both tubes from the flame keeping them as horizontal as possible while ensuring that no liquid gets too close to either opening. Now, working as close as you can to the flame, raise the larger tube until the opening of the small tube is right over it. Acting quickly, pour the contents directly into the larger tube. Do not rest the small tube on the big tube. Get them close together, but do not bring them in contact with each other. Pour the liquid directly into the center of the opening. Be careful not to spill any on the outside.

STERILE TRANSFER: LIQUID

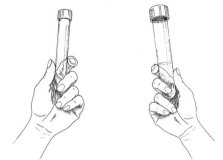

1. Before transfering the liquid from the smaller tube on the left to the larger tube on the right, make sure that the yeast is completely loose and that the CO_2 has been driven out.

2. With the right hand, grab the closure of the left tube. Unscrew the left tube and bring the opening to the zone of the flame.

3. Flame the opening of the left tube. Make sure that the closure in the right hand is always facing down.

4. Keeping the left tube opening near the flame, place the cap of the right tube in the palm of the left hand. With the right hand, unscrew the larger tube.

5. Bring the opening of the larger tube to the flame. Keep the left tube close to the flame, and always keep both closures facing down.

STERILE TRANSFER: LIQUID

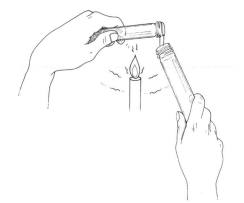

6. Working as close as possible to the flame, pour the contents of the left tube into the right tube. Try to pour right in the middle of the tube. Do not let the tubes touch each other.

7. Flame the opening of the large tube.

8. Bring the opening of the large tube back to its cap, and screw it in. Keep the opening of the small tube within the zone of the flame.

9. Flame the opening of the small tube, bring it to its closure, and screw it in.

10. The left tube still holds a few drops of liquid, enough for a microscope check. The right tube should show signs of fermentation within four to six hours.

7.5

Closing the tubes

Once the transfer is finished, flame both openings again. You now close the tubes by reversing the opening procedure. Put the closure back on the larger tube. To do this, bring the tube opening toward the cap, and twist the tube into the cap. When capped, proceed in the same way with the empty tube. When both tubes are closed, put them in their respective racks.

Doing it the first time

When I first started doing this operation, it was very hard to perform smoothly. I even needed someone else to help me. Each of us would hold a tube. After a while, I got the hang of it and could do it alone. This operation requires a bit of practice. It is not difficult, but coordinating the independent movements of two hands is sometimes difficult. Most people to whom I have demonstrated this procedure were able to perform the transfer adequately in a relatively short period of time.

DOING IT WITH BIGGER JARS

This procedure is fairly simple when transferring between test tubes, but when you transfer larger quantities you will need help. When I propagate yeast in commercial quantities, I need another pair of hands. Pouring one liter of fermenting wort into a four-liter vessel is difficult. To hold both vessels firmly, you require more than two hands.

Getting the flame to the opening

With larger bottles it is sometimes difficult to maneuver the bottle opening near the flame. To facilitate this, I recommend using a Bunsen burner or propane torch. Open the bottle, and with the other hand grasp the burner or torch and bring it to the opening. Flame the opening while your partner opens the larger flask. Now flame both openings and transfer the liquid. Reflame the opening and then close it.

Chapter VIII: **Pouring plates**

Plate usage

Preparing petri plates is one of the fundamental tasks required by the brewing microbiologist. In a commercial brewery, plates are the principal tool used for detecting the presence of bacteria in either beer or wort, as well as in the rinsing water and the surrounding air. They are quite commonly used in research and development laboratories for the preliminary selection of individual colonies in yeast culture. However, to succeed in either of these activities it is essential that the plates be properly poured.

Types of dishes

For almost a century, petri plates were made of high quality heat-resistant glass. Nowadays, however, advances in the development of plastics have made the glass plates almost obsolete. Today, petri plates are made of a neutral plastic. The plates are sterilized at the factory by gamma ray irradiation. Stacked in groups of twenty and placed in sterilized plastic bags, they remain sterile until used. These "twenty packs" are put in boxes containing usually five hundred individual plates. This quantity is outrageously large for most enterprising individuals and even the majority of small scale commercial brewers. For some, it represents a lifetime supply. For others, this quantity may last a few years. However, because of their low price I recommend their usage. Ten quality glass petri plates cost almost as much as 500 plastic units. In addition, glass dishes need to be sterilized each time. Preferably, you should use the entire bag of twenty plates all at once. However, this is not practical for the small brewer. Carefully remove from the bag the quantity of plates required, and then close the bag with tape before you put it away.

Evaluating your needs

When preparing to pour plates, calculate ahead of time the quantity that you really need. You do not need to make more than what is required for immediate usage. In fact, if you make more, you will probably end up having to throw them away before you use them. Because they are not sealed and are in contact with the ambiant air, they will dry up within a short while. Even if you seal them with tape or some other means, they will loose humidity. They might look good, but they will have become hard and too solid to be useful. Keeping them in a frost-free refrigerator is a quick way to make them unsuitable. When poured and dried, the plates should be kept in a sealed bag in a cool place. As a rule of thumb, do not make more than what you can use in one or two weeks. It is much easier to prepare the wort agar mixture in individual small bottles that you can use as needed, than to prepare many plates and throw half of them away.

PREPARING THE AGAR

When making plates, there are two ways to proceed. You either pour the plates with wort agar liquid that you have just sterilized, or pour them with a mixture that was previously sterilized and that you have just remelted. In both cases, you have to lower the agar temperature before pouring. If it is too hot, a lot of condensation will form on the cover of the plate. Although in all cases you have some condensation, you should aim for a minimum. Also make sure that the mixture has not cooled down too much.

Cooling the nutrient agar

An easy way to cool down the mixture quickly is to cool the flasks or bottles under running hot tap water (described in the section *Cooling the liquid agar* in Chapter XI). Household hot tap water is usually between 50°C and 60°C. This prevents glass breakage and overcooling. The addition of a small quantity of cold water brings the temperature down further. As soon as you can hold the flask in your bare hand, put it against your cheek. It should feel comfortably warm. At this temperature agar is almost ready to gel, so you have to act swiftly.

Make sure that the agar is completely liquid

When liquefying previously sterilized agar, make sure that it is completely liquefied. At times it seems completely liquid, but in the middle of the liquid there may still be a lump. There is nothing more frustrating than having to interrupt plate pouring because the liquid suddenly flows with lumps in it.

Prepare ahead of time

Small brewers should always plan the pouring of their plates ahead of time. The ideal conditions for this task are not always present. Molds from airborne contamination are the most common cause of infection that ruins plates. Pasteur was the first to demonstrate that microbes, bacteria and molds are carried in great quantities by dust particles floating about in the air. Therefore, the utmost care must be taken to prepare plates in an environment that is as dust and draft-free as possible.

How large laboratories do it

Some large laboratories have a special clean room in which to perform this task. Others do it in a highly secure cabinet called a "laminar flow hood". This device is a covered cabinet that is opened on the side facing the operator. Sterile filtered air is vented through the hood such that there is no turbulence in the flow. The air flows through slowly, without any cross currents. None of the ambient air is capable of flowing back in. Working with such an apparatus ensures complete success for the competent worker. However, the price and the room required for a laminar flow hood puts it out of reach of the majority. Only laboratories who are conducting this type of operation and other sterile manipulations on a continual basis really need them.

The ideal condition for everyone

There are many ways of ensuring success, even under ordinary conditions. Old brewing microbiology textbooks recommended pouring plates as the first task in the morning. During the night there is no movement or activity in the room. As long as the windows are closed shut, the ambient air is quite still in the morning. Better yet is Monday morning after a weekend off. Common sources of failure are open windows, room or central air conditioning and hot air heating systems. Hired help engaged in cleaning often use a vacuum cleaner. This is the greatest device ever invented to get dust up in the air.

The worst conditions

Most small commercial breweries are chronically short of space. They also tend to have quite a number of fans, motors and air circulating devices that keep the surrounding air in a state of perpetual motion. In combination with cigarette smoke and a humid environment caused by the hot vapors of brewing and washing, this is a sure invitation to failure. Amateur brewers sometimes find laboratory operations easier to perform than pub or microbrewers. They can easily find a place in their house where they can perform the manipulations under appropriate conditions. Some commercial brewers delegate to a responsible person the task of doing routine microbiological work at home.

What can go wrong

Many authors have created scare conditions by claiming that basic microbiological manipulations cannot be done unless you have access to a sterile chamber and laminar flow hood. In the situation of a microbiology laboratory that performs work of a medical nature, I would agree that this is important, because it often handles germs of infectious diseases. However, it is quite easy to perform this work if you take the ordinary precautions described above. In most cases, molds are the cause of plate contamination. If this happens, simply throw the plates away. Experience has shown that ordinary skilled people who perform this type of work conscientiously will achieve success consistently.

SETTING UP YOUR WORK AREA

Once you have selected a place and time most suitable for pouring your plates, the task itself requires only a few minutes. Prepare a clean flat surface ahead of time. A good wiping with rubbing alcohol is recommended. Have at your disposal rubber or insulated gloves and a flame source. Although you do not have to flame sterilize the opening of the flask that comes out of the autoclave, it is still good practice to do so. It should always be done when you are using a container that has been previously sterilized, and that you have just warmed up to liquefy its contents.

How many plates should I make?

One hundred ml of an agar wort mixture is adequate for pouring five or six plates. The petri dish size most suitable for yeast work is a diameter of 100 mm and a depth of 15 mm. A plate that contains between 15 to 20 ml of media is considered adequate. When poured and set, the depth of the media should be 3 mm. However, the working surface you use may not be perfectly level, and your plates may have more media on one side than the other. Such variations are normal and acceptable. This is why you sometimes end up with one more or one less plate than expected.

The actual pouring

- Lay the plates down in a half circle in front of you.
- Make sure the agar is completely liquefied. If the agar is solid liquefy it by following the method described in the section *Liquefying the agar* in Chapter XI.
- Do the temperature "cheek test", then proceed.
- Remove the aluminum foil that protects the opening of the flask.
- Remove the closure by grabbing it between your small finger and the palm of the right hand. Do this near the flame.
- Place the flask opening near or very close to the flame. If you are using a flask directly from the autoclave, just hold it there for a few seconds. However, if it is agar that you have just liquefied, make sure that you flame the flask all the way around to burn off any dust particles that might have adhered to the surface.
- Lift the cover from a plate with the right hand, and pour into it with the left hand an amount of liquid that covers a little bit more than two thirds of the bottom. Although the agar is liquid, it is still viscous. Prepare to stop as soon as two thirds of the bottom surface is filled. The agar will run over to fill the rest of the dish in the following seconds.
- Put the lid back on. With the right hand, impart a slight circular motion to the dish if the surface is not completely filled with agar. This will take care of any unfilled areas. Be careful to do this smoothly, or the agar will adhere to the sides and the lid. In most cases these unfilled spots are caused by pouring a bit less agar than is needed, or by working on a surface that is not level.
- Continue in the same way with the next plate. Pouring five to six plates should take approximately 10 to 15 seconds. In the event that you pour more than six plates, push aside some that are already filled. If you have to stop pouring, bring the opening of the bottle back to the flame.

Condensation, and how to minimize it

When you put the lids back on the plates, you will notice condensation on the covers. This is absolutely normal. Just leave the plates on the table until they are set. When they are ready, stack them three to four high. Put a rubber band around them. Turn them upside down, and lay them in a warm spot in the upside down position. The condensation is now on the bottom lid and in contact with the ambient air. To accelerate condensation removal, place the plates in a warm area. I find that a good place is on top of a household refrigerator. If you have a cupboard above your refrigerator, place them in there. If the agar was cooled down sufficiently when poured, the condensation will usually disappear overnight.

Using and storing

When the condensation is gone the plates are ready to be used. Plates poured at the right temperature leave very little condensation, and can be used immediately. If you decide to use them in a few days, place them in a sealed container and lay them in a cool place.

Plates should be used during the following two weeks. When inoculated they will remain in good condition for a further two weeks. This gives a total shelf life of four weeks. This is considered normal and sufficient.

POURING PLATES

1. Assemble the quantity of plates needed and the wort agar flask on the work table.

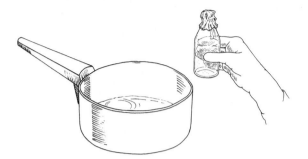

2. If the agar is solid, liquefy it in a hot water bath. Place the bottle in a pot. Pour enough hot water in the pot and bring to a boil. Verify that all the agar has liquefied before proceeding further.

3. Have a flame source ready.

4. Remove the aluminum foil that protects the opening.

5. With the little finger grasp the closure, open the flask and immediately...

6. Place the flask opening in the flame.

POURING PLATES

7. Lift the plate cover slightly and pour 15 to 20 ml of wort agar. The liquid should cover at least two thirds of the surface.

8. If needed, give the plate a gentle twirl to distribute the agar evenly.

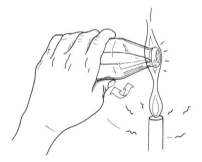

9. Proceed immediately to the next plate. Normally, five to six plates can be poured in succession.

10. If you have to stop, place the bottle opening back in the flame. If you do not pour all the agar, recap the bottle.

11. After pouring, condensation will form on the cover. Do not move the plates until they have solidified.

12. Stack the plates one on top of the other. Invert them so that a lid (with condensation) is at the bottom. Attach with an elastic band and keep warm. Condensation will disappear overnight.

CHAPTER IX: PLATING A YEAST SUSPENSION

THE PURPOSE OF PLATING

All fermenting liquid contains a great quantity of yeast cells. At the start of fermentation an acceptable quantity is normally 5 to 10 million cells per ml. Toward the end, this figure can go as high as 60 million cell per ml. If you take a sample containing this amount of yeast cells and examine it under the microscope, you will find that the cells are so close together, it is almost impossible to get a good look at an individual cell or group of cells.

This book deals only with manipulations that give significant results without the use of a microscope. At times however, we will mention the results of microscopic observations as a reference.

Ways of obtaining individual colonies with plates

To successfully investigate cells on an individual or small group basis, you have to dilute them. Two methods can be used to accomplish this easily.

The first method consists in taking a sterile sample directly with the inoculating needle and spreading it out on a plate.

The second method consists in first diluting a sample in sterile water and then spreading it out on a plate.

Which method is most suitable?

The first method leads to wide streaks of growing microorganisms on the plate. It looks like a carpet of yeast. It is difficult or impossible to select well defined colonies. Those that are present are normally quite close to one another and are quite small.

The second method gets the colonies well separated on the first spread. The colonies are easy to select individually. The results in both cases can be the same. However, I prefer the second method, as it is more precise and gives better results.

Another means of separating individual cells is to pour an agar solution over a yeast suspension in a sterile petri dish. This manipulation is useful when you want to know how many living cells are present in a suspension. This operation will be dealt with in detail in Chapter XI.

REMARKS ON PLATING

First, let's look at the proper way of spreading a liquid suspension on a plate, commonly referred to as plating.

The whole operation can be summarized as follows: plating involves taking a sample of a microorganism suspension and placing it in a sterile manner over the media surface enclosed in a petri dish. The suspension is then spread out over the surface of the media to obtain individual colonies growing separately from each other.

Many authors have given different details regarding this type of operation. They all have their significance and merits, depending on the type of bacteria or cells you are working with. Microbiologists working in hospital laboratories or medical research institutes have to be very careful with manipulations of this nature, because they are often working with pathogenic germs. Strict precautionary measures must be observed. Let's not forget that all of these manipulations were originally devised by medical researchers, and were subsequently adapted to fermentation investigation.

In the case of brewery fermentation and operations, we are not dealing with anything of a dangerous or infectious nature. Performing the following manipulations in a suitable environment will give good results on a consistent basis.

THE OPERATION, STEP BY STEP

- Put the plate upside down on the working table, that is, with the smaller half containing the media on top.
- Flame sterilize the opening of the test tube holding the yeast suspension, and draw a loopful, with the inoculating loop.
- Reflame and close the test tube.
- With the left hand, take the half of the plate that contains the media, lift it up and hold it vertically.
- Starting at the top of the plate, streak the loopful smoothly across it in an elongated "S" manner until you reach about one third of the way down from the top.
- Turn the plate approximately 60 degrees counterclockwise, and repeat the streaking motion. In between streaks, keep the inoculating loop close to the plate.
- Now go over the streak line that you have just made. Continue in the same manner, going down one third of the way from the top.
- Turn the plate 60 degrees counterclockwise again, and repeat a third time. Streak the surface of the plate that you have not gone over previously.
- Replace the half of the plate that contains the media back onto its lid.

From now on, keep the plate with the media on top. Turning clockwise or counterclockwise is a matter of personal preference and comfort.

Points to watch for

Is there enough yeast?

It is very important that you do not reinoculate or sterilize the loop between streaks. It seems that there is nothing on the loop. In fact, there are very few cells on it. But this is what you want: a limited number of cells that will grow distinctly and separately from each other. You have to do this operation to appreciate its results.

Practice makes perfect

Before you attempt to perform this operation, you may think that it is a long and difficult manipulation to perform without incurring infection. The first time you attempt it you will probably fumble. In reality, the whole operation can be performed by a skilled operator in just four to five seconds.

What about the danger of contamination?

Some people would say that by holding the plate in the air, you are submitting it to all kinds of airborne contamination. Although it might appear so, practically speaking this is untrue. First, you are holding the plate vertically. The chance that a microorganism present in the air would land on a vertical plate is quite slim. Microorganisms are more likely to fall on the exposed half of the plate lying on the table. Keeping the media half on top will prevent possible contamination, since it eliminates the possibility of any stray microorganism falling back down on the media surface.

How fast will the yeast grow?

Another point in your favor is that yeast is a rapidly growing organism. Once you have spread it out on a plate, it will show visible signs of growth within twenty-four hours. In three to four days you will be able to select and pick fully developed colonies. Any strange and undesirable microorganism that might have fallen on the plate will most likely be a mold spore. It will be overcome or at least impeded in its development by the rapidly growing yeast.

At what temperature should I keep the plate?

Plates have a short shelf life. I consider that a properly made and inoculated plate has a shelf life of about two to three weeks. Suppose that you are using a freshly poured plate that is one day old. As soon as you have inoculated the plate, you have to keep it warm for the yeast colony to grow quickly. The best temperature is around 30°C, which is most favorable for yeast growth.

How long is the plate useful for?

Because of the warmth, water from the media is slowly evaporating. The evaporation is insignificant during the first week. You have plenty of time to pick cells and store them away. The yeast will continue to grow for some time, but the work of the plate is over. The best means of preserving the plates is to keep them in a sealed plastic bag in a cool basement. I have kept plates in this manner for up to four weeks. This allows you to further examine the growing of the cells.

If kept warm, the media will shrink visibly after about two weeks. If kept cold and unsealed in a refrigerator, the same drying out will occur. At times you might see some molds developing on the edge of the plate. This is nothing to worry about. The initial purpose, to spread out the yeast and pick individual colonies, has been achieved.

What about sealing the plate?

Some people go to the trouble of sealing the two halves of the plate together with masking tape or "parafilm". I personally consider this a wasted effort. It merely delays the drying effect for a short while. Plates should not be considered a means of keeping cultures. They are just a useful intermediary tool.

HOW TO OBTAIN SINGLE COLONIES WITHOUT DILUTING

If a great number of yeast cells were present in the yeast suspension streaked on the plate, a solid accumulation of yeast colonies will grow. There will be very few individual cell colonies on the plate. Those present will most likely be very small. This is quite common when the plate is streaked with actively fermenting wort.

To get well defined single colonies, streak a second plate right after the first one. Do this second streaking without reinoculating your loop. After streaking the first plate, lay it back down on the table. Immediately pick up another one and repeat the same streaking motion three times across the plate. Between streaks do not put the loop in the flame. Just keep it near the flame. Do not pick up any more yeast suspension than what is left clinging to the loop. It might seem that there is nothing left, but there are a few cells attached to it. The streak mark will be less visible on the second plate than on the first one.

In a few days, you will be rewarded with distinct individual colonies. I often use this method when I have spare plates to use before they age too much. No special preparation is needed. It is a good method when working with only one yeast strain.

Another way to obtain individual colonies

If I do not have any spare plates or want to do a larger number of plates, I use a different procedure to obtain the same result.

This second method entails taking a known amount of yeast suspension and diluting it until you have the right concentration. This way you obtain well separated colonies on the first plate. This operation is called a dilution, which is the subject of the next chapter.

PLATING A YEAST SUSPENSION

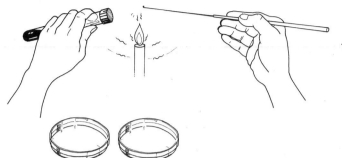

1. The tube in the left hand holds well homogenized fermenting wort. The flame is on. The inoculating loop is in the right hand. Two wort agar plates are on the left with the media half on top.

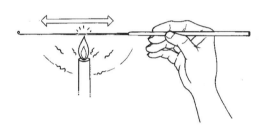

2. Starting at the tip, flame the inoculating loop all the way to the gripping jaws.

3. Keep the loop in the zone of the flame, and bring the tube to the palm of your right hand.

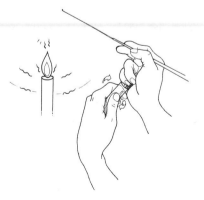

4. Grasp the cap with the little finger.

5. Unscrew the tube by twisting the left hand.

PLATING A YEAST SUSPENSION

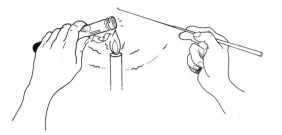

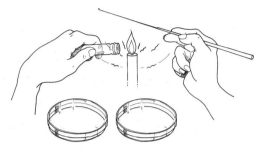

6. Holding the tube at a slight angle, bring it near the flame. Twist the tube all the way around in the flame. Keep the loop 5 to 6 cm away from the flame.

7. Withdraw the tube to about 5 or 6 cm away from the flame. Keep the tube at an angle to prevent liquid from flowing out.

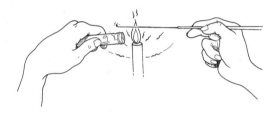

8. Plunge the wire inside the tube, and twist it lightly in the fermenting liquid. Do not touch the inside of the tube.

9. Carefully withdraw the wire with a drop of fermenting liquid on the loop. Keep the loop approximately 5 to 6 cm away from the flame.

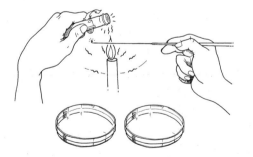

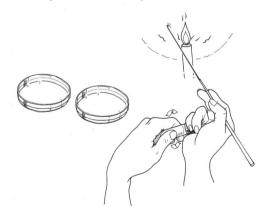

10. Twist and turn the tube in the flame gain. Keep the loop approximately 5 to 6 cm away from the flame.

11. Screw the tube back in its cap. All this time, keep the loop 5 to 6 cm away from the flame.

PLATING A YEAST SUSPENSION

12. Place the tube in the test tube rack.

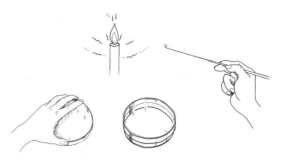

13. With the left hand, take the media half of the petri dish and place it in a vertical position.

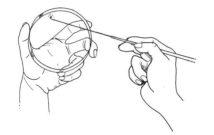

14. Starting at the top of the plate, drag the loop in an elongated "S" manner. Go one third of the way down. Keep the loop near the plate. Do not flame the loop.

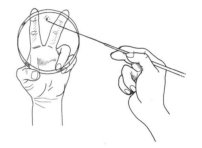

15. Rotate the plate approximately 60 degrees with your fingers. Starting at the top again, proceed in the same manner. You are now going over the first series of streaks. Go one third of the way down. Keep the loop near the plate. Do not flame the loop.

16. Turn the plate again approximately 60 degrees. Starting at the top, proceed in the same manner. You are now going over the first and second series of streaks. Go one third of the way down. Streak the rest of the plate.

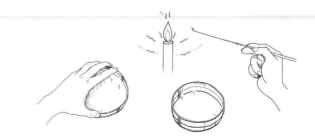

17. Immediately replace the media half of the plate in its lid. Place the tip of the loop in the zone of the flame, but not in the flame.

PLATING A YEAST SUSPENSION

18. With the left hand, take the media half of a second petri dish, and hold it in an vertical position. Do not flame or reinoculate the loop.

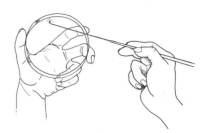

19. Starting at the top of the plate, drag the loop in an elongated "S" manner, exactly as for the first plate. There is almost no yeast present and the streak marks are less visible.

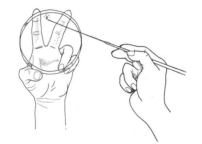

20. Rotate the plate approximately 60 degrees with your fingers, and proceed exactly as for the first plate. Very few yeast cells are on the loop now.

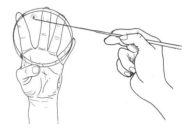

21. Turn the plate again approximately 60 degrees. Starting at the top, proceed in the same manner. You are now going over the first and second series of streaks. This last streaking will produce well defined colonies.

22. Immediately replace the media half of the plate in its lid.

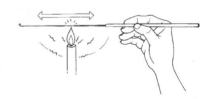

23. Flame the loop and put it away.

PLATING: THE STREAKING MOTION

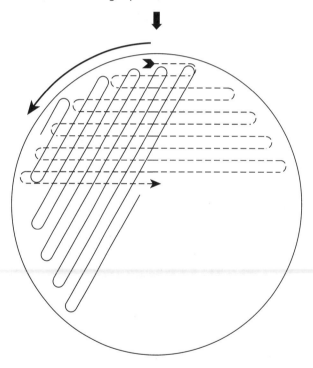

1. Holding the plate vertically, streak the fermenting liquid across the plate following the illustrated zigzag pattern. Go down a distance equal to approximately one third of the plate diameter.

2. Rotate the plate approximately 60 degrees and repeat the streaking motion. Do not reinoculate the loop or put it in the flame. Spreading the first streak over a sterile portion of the plate dilutes the fermenting liquid.

3. Rotate the plate again approximately 60 degrees and repeat the same streaking motion. Streak the remaining surface of the plate. Recap the plate afterward.

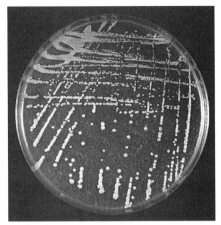

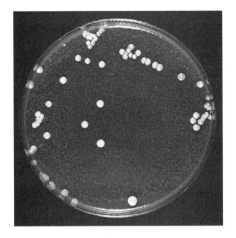

1. Plate streaked directly from a 10 ml fermenting test tube. Colonies are very close to one another. The few isolated individual colonies are small, because they are too crowded.

2. Second plate streaked without reinoculating the loop after streaking the first plate. Individual colonies are well separated. They are bigger and have lots of room to spread. These are good subjects for reculturing.

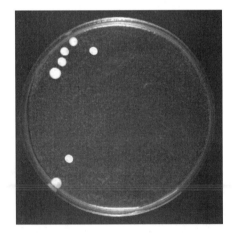

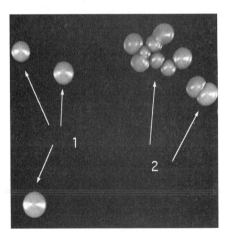

3. Another plate steaked with a diluted yeast suspension. The dilution was made by diluting only one loopful of fermenting wort in 3 ml of sterile water. All the plates on this page were made from a wort treated with Irish moss. Notice the numerous specs in the background.

4. Plate streaked from a diluted yeast suspension. Close-up of colonies:
Colonies 1 are well separated and growing vigorously. These are good subjects for selection.
Colonies 2 are too crowded and are not good subject for selection.

Chapter X: DILUTION

THE NEED FOR A DILUTION

A solution in either active or finished fermentation holds a great number of cells. The same is true of a solution that contains a combination of yeast and bacteria. You do not know how many cells are present in the liquid. Determining the number of cells is what this chapter is all about.

Practical ways of counting yeast cells

When dealing only with yeast, there are two possibilities. First, you can physically count the number of cells using a counting chamber, or second, you can count the number of colonies growing on a plate. Because the use of a counting chamber requires a microscope, it will be covered in the second volume of this book.

To facilitate counting, the yeast suspension must first be diluted to reduce the number of individual cells present. This way, when the diluted suspension is plated out, the individual cells are able to grow separately from each other in a quantity small enough to permit counting.

Even when you use a counting chamber, you still need to make a dilution to obtain a concentration level suitable for counting. The procedure is exactly the same. It varies only after the dilution has been carried out. With a counting chamber you count immediately. Without one, the microorganisms have to grow before you can count. This entails a delay of at least four to five days.

WHAT YOU NEED TO PERFORM A DILUTION

Preparing the material

The following dilution procedure is the type commonly done in brewing. Before starting, make sure that you have enough of the required supplies:

- One 10 ml pipette
- Five 1 ml pipettes
- One empty sterile test tube
- Five sterile test tubes, each holding 9 ml of sterile water
- A suspension of microorganisms

How to choose a pipette

The only operation that we have not covered so far is pipetting.

A pipette is a graduated tube used like a straw. It is used to transfer a fixed quantity of liquid from one container to another. Pipettes are sold presterilized and ready to use. They are wrapped in a plastic covering, and should be stored in a dust-free cabinet.

For the kind of work that is routinely performed in brewing microbiology, pipettes of 10 ml and 1 ml are all that is required. They are usually sold as throwaway models, and are made of either plastic or glass. Washable and reusable glass pipettes are also available. Pipettes have a cotton plug at one end that prevents the entry of bacteria from your mouth.

Personally, I feel that the throwaway model in glass is a better buy. After usage they can be cleaned and reused for many purposes. They are the best tool available for precisely measuring a small quantity of liquid. They can also be resterilized for subsequent use.

The only inconvenience with pipettes is that they are commonly sold in astronomical quantities by laboratory supply houses. A minimum order can be a lifetime supply.

Notes on resterilizing pipettes

Throwaway glass pipettes can be easily resterilized. If you have not wetted the cotton plug, it can also be reused. Otherwise, you will have to make and insert a new plug.

The pipettes should be thoroughly cleaned immediately after usage, as described in the section *Cleaning glassware* in Chapter XII.

Once cleaned, let them dry and put them away.

Because hot air sterilization is done in the oven, wait till you have enough pipettes to warrant it.

Wrap the pipettes in aluminum foil individually or in small bundles of five; which is the quantity usually required for a dilution.

Fold the end of the foil over the pipette. Identify which end is the mouth opening.

Preheat the oven to 175°C.

Lay down the wrapped pipettes on the oven rack, spacing the bundles evenly.

Keep them in the oven for at least 30 minutes, then turn the oven off.

When cooled, remove the pipettes and store them in a clean closed box.

To use, lift a corner of the aluminum foil at the mouth end. Remove one pipette and reclose the foil.

Use immediately, in the same manner as a new sterile pipette. If another one is needed, wait until the moment you will use it before removing it from the foil. Never take more than one pipette at a time from a bundle. This will ensure that all pipettes remain sterile.

It is easy to check if the sterilization temperature has been reached. The cotton plug at the mouth end will be yellow in color. This means that the proper sterilization temperature has been reached and maintained. The plug should not be white, brown or darker.

BEFORE STARTING

Make sure that the suspension is completely homogenized. To get all the microorganisms well spread out in the liquid, you must twirl it around considerably. This can be quite difficult to accomplish when the yeast adheres tightly on the bottom of the tube, and makes clumps when loosened. When yeast is like this, it is at times impossible to get the clumps broken, unless you have an expensive laboratory type shaking apparatus.

Counting yeast cells is usually made at the start of fermentation or in the preparation of a starter. At this stage, the clumping activity of yeast is greatly reduced, and it is quite easy to get a uniform suspension. The best time to do this is right after you add a bottle of sterile wort to a starter. Wait half an hour. Then the yeast cells will have separated from each other quite well.

HOW TO PERFORM STERILE TRANSFER WITH A PIPETTE

As soon as the solution appears homogeneous, remove exactly 10 ml and transfer it to a sterile empty test tube. Proceed as follows:

- First, carefully remove the wrapping from a 10 ml pipette. Follow the manufacturer's instructions.
- Bring the tip of the pipette to the zone of the flame, and keep the tip almost in the flame (be careful if using a plastic pipette).

- Open the flask of fermented liquid in the zone of the flame, and flame the flask opening.
- Plunge the pipette into the flask.
- Using your mouth, suck on the pipette to draw up the liquid. Before you start drawing it, note the location of the 10 ml mark.
- Keeping an eye on the liquid and on the mark, draw up the liquid until it is approximately 1 to 2 ml over the 10 ml line.
- Put your index finger on the tip of the pipette.
- Slowly release the pressure so that the liquid flows back down to the 10 ml mark.
- Take the pipette out of the flask, and hold it in an almost horizontal position.
- At all times, keep your index finger over the opening and the tip of the pipette in the zone of the flame.
- Flame and close the flask, and pick up an empty sterile test tube. Open the test tube and flame it.
- Introduce the tip of the pipette into the tube and release your finger from the opening. This will let the liquid flow into the test tube.
- Flame and close the test tube.
- Put away the now empty pipette in a suitable container. The hydrometer jar is appropriate. Do not put it on the table.

Doing the first dilution

You now have a sterile test tube that holds exactly 10 ml of microorganism suspension. The next step consists in drawing exactly 1 ml of this suspension and transferring it to another test tube that contains 9 ml of distilled water. This tube will have been previously autoclaved to ensure sterility.

Following the same pipetting procedure, draw 1 ml of the fermenting solution. This time use a 1 ml pipette, and transfer the liquid to the 9 ml test tubes. This is now a dilution of 1 to 10.

Getting the dilution completely homogeneous

Holding the tube by the tube walls, swirl it gently to ensure that the suspension gets thoroughly mixed. Some technicians perform this mixing with the pipette when filling the test tube. They repeatedly draw in and blow out a small amount of the suspension in the pipette. This gives an excellent mixing. When mixing in this way, you have to be careful not to get the cotton plug wet.

Diluting further

Now take the first dilution test tube and repeat the same procedure. For this transfer, use a new sterilized pipette of the same 1 ml capacity. The dilution is now 1 to 100.

Proceed this way four to five times until you obtain the level of dilution you are aiming for.

THE MATHEMATICS OF DILUTION

Suppose that you have a fermenting solution estimated to hold approximately 15 million yeast cells per ml.

The first dilution brings this down to 1.5 million cells per ml,

The second dilution: 150,000 cells per ml,

The third dilution: 15,000 cells per ml,

The fourth dilution 1500 cells per ml,

The fifth dilution 150 cells per ml.

This is a ratio that permits counting. The next step will show you how to prepare the materials for the counting operation.

SERIAL DILUTION

To obtain a good homogeneous yeast suspension, it is best to perform this operation approximately half an hour after adding fresh wort to the flask. This way, the yeast cells will be well separated from each other. Follow the pipetting instructions on the next four pages to make this first transfer.

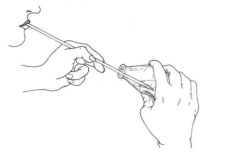 

1. Using a sterile pipette, draw 10 ml of the fermenting wort and...

2. Transfer it into an empty sterile test tube.

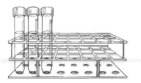

3. Place the test tube in the test tube rack. Ahead of time, prepare a quantity of test tubes that each contain 9 ml of sterile water.

Although it is good practice to use a new sterile pipette for each transfer, the series of transfers can be done with only one pipette if you are experienced and very careful. Two errors are possible: not measuring the quantity of liquid precisely, and leaving behind at the top of the pipette a drop of concentrated suspension. Some operators thoroughly mix the liquid by repeatedly sucking in and blowing out the liquid between the test tube and the pipette. This also has the advantage of mixing the suspension completely.

Pipette Manipulation

1. Make sure that the yeast suspension is completely homogenized.

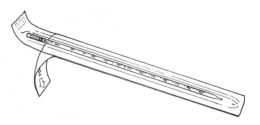

2. Carefully remove the wrapping from the pipette by peeling away the top few inches.

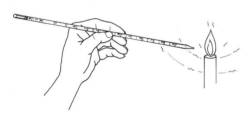

3. Take the pipette out of the wrapping, and place the tip in the zone of the flame.

4. Take the test tube containing the homogeneous yeast suspension and...

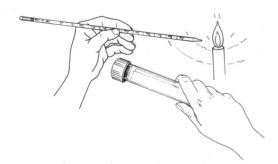

5. Keeping the tip of the pipette in the zone of the flame, remove the cap from the tube.

6. Flame the test tube opening thoroughly.

PIPETTE MANIPULATION

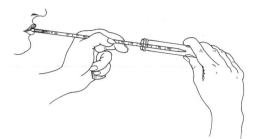

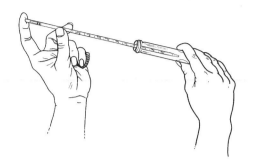

7. Plunge the pipette into the tube and suck in the liquid. Draw the liquid one or two marks above the 1 ml mark.

8. Put your index finger on the opening of the pipette. This will prevent the liquid from flowing back in.

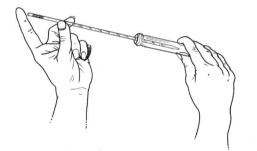

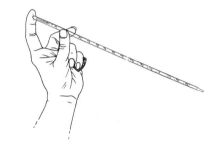

9. Slowly release the pressure of the finger. Let the excess liquid flow back in until the liquid reaches the 1 ml mark. It is easier to do this by keeping the tip of the pipette in the liquid.

10. Reapply pressure on your finger. Take the pipette out of the test tube, and keep its tip in the zone of the flame.

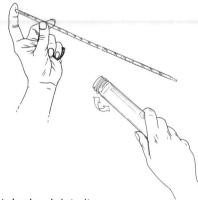

11. Flame the opening of the test tube.

12. Screw the tube back into its cap.

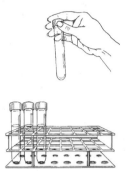

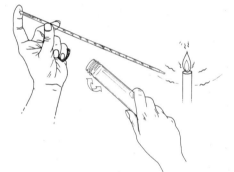

13. Replace the tube in the test tube rack.

14. Take a test tube containing 9 ml of sterile water.

15. Remove the cap. All this time, keep the tip of the pipette in the zone of the flame.

16. Flame the mouth of the test tube.

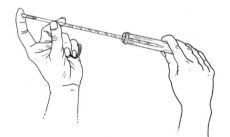

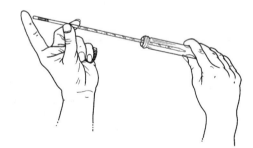

17. Plunge the pipette into the tube.

18. Release the pressure from your finger, and the liquid will flow out.

PIPETTE MANIPULATION

19. Flame the opening of the test tube again.

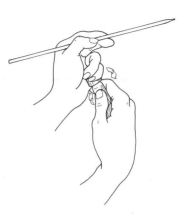

20. Screw the tube back into its cap.

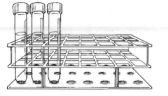

21. Put the test tube in the tube rack.

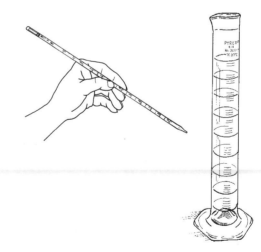

22. Place the now empty pipette in a suitable container.

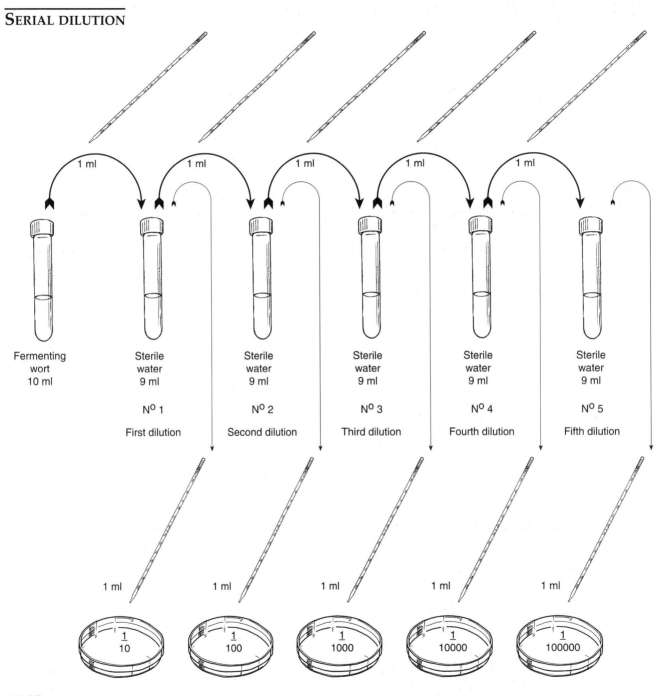

1 ml   1 ml   1 ml   1 ml   1 ml

Fermenting   Sterile   Sterile   Sterile   Sterile   Sterile
wort   water   water   water   water   water
10 ml   9 ml   9 ml   9 ml   9 ml   9 ml

N° 1   N° 2   N° 3   N° 4   N° 5

First dilution   Second dilution Third dilution   Fourth dilution Fifth dilution

1 ml   1 ml   1 ml   1 ml   1 ml

$\frac{1}{10}$ $\frac{1}{100}$ $\frac{1}{1000}$ $\frac{1}{10000}$ $\frac{1}{100000}$

10.12

CHAPTER XI: THE POUR PLATE METHOD

The second method used for obtaining separate colonies of yeast or other microorganisms is to mix a diluted suspension with liquefied agar directly onto plates. Upon setting, the microorganisms will start to grow. The advantage of this method is that you obtain a very good separation of individual cells, as well as clearly defined individual colonies.

The following manipulation is fairly simple to do. However, to make the results more significant I recommend that you prepare at least two plates of each dilution.

WHAT IS REQUIRED TO PERFORM THIS OPERATION

- A prepared vial of sterile wort agar mixture
- A prepared series of yeast dilutions
- Two or more 1 ml sterile pipettes
- Two or more petri dishes

LIQUEFYING THE AGAR

To accomplish this manipulation, we need the agar nutrient mixture in the liquid state, but at a low temperature. If the agar temperature is too high, it will simply kill all the microorganisms upon mixing. Because you cannot stick a thermometer in the sterile agar, your sense of touch is the best way to check the temperature.

Use freshly sterilized wort agar or a previously prepared mixture. If the agar solution has been prepared ahead of time, bring it to the liquefying temperature, that is, above 95°C. Once it is completely liquefied, cool it down to just a few degrees above the setting temperature of 45°C.

COOLING THE LIQUID AGAR

Cooling down the agar solution is easily accomplished in two steps.

First step: lower the temperature to 60°C

First lower the temperature of the agar from nearly boiling point to about 60°C. An easy way to do this is to cool the melted agar bottle under running hot household water. Domestic hot water tanks usually maintain the temperature at 50°C to 60°C. You can check this with a thermometer. Once the agar bottle has cooled down and stabilized at the hot water temperature, it will be more comfortable to handle.

Second step: lower the temperature to below 50°C

Slowly add a bit of cold water to the cooling bath to further lower the temperature. Stick a thermometer into the bath as a guide. When the cooling bath has stabilized for a few minutes at a temperature below 50°C, take the flask and carefully place it against your cheek. If you can leave it there comfortably for four to five seconds, the temperature is right for pouring. You now must act quickly and surely.

TRANSFERRING THE YEAST TO THE EMPTY PETRI DISH

The first operation consists in a sterile transfer of one ml of the thoroughly mixed yeast dilution that you estimate will yield the best results. To accomplish this, use the one ml pipette.

Following the basic pipetting operation described earlier, transfer one ml of solution from the test tube or flask and place it right in the middle of an empty petri dish. Repeat the same procedure for a second dish. Some technicians prepare up to five plates to get a better average result.

POURING THE LIQUID AGAR OVER THE YEAST

As soon as the plates are inoculated, open the liquefied agar vial, flame the opening and pour 15 to 20 ml of the liquefied agar right over the deposited 1 ml yeast dilution. Evaluating the right quantity will come with experience. As soon as you have poured the agar, bring the bottle back to the flame.

Mixing the agar with yeast

Immediately swirl the liquid gently in the plate to thoroughly mix the agar with the yeast suspension. Be careful not to swirl too briskly, or the agar will adhere to the top lid. A gentle swirl of five seconds is usually sufficient. Wait a few minutes; the agar and yeast suspension mixture will solidify.

When solidified, put a rubber band around the plates and place them in an incubating area. Any place that has temperature close to 30°C is adequate. The top of a household refrigerator or hot water tank is available to everyone. Check with a thermometer to find the most suitable place.

OBSERVING THE GROWTH

If you have executed the operation properly, expect to see visible specks of growth within forty-eight hours, and evident colonies within three days. When no further new growth appears, usually after six days, start counting the number of colonies that are present and imbedded in the plate. If no signs of growth are evident after four days, you have poured the agar at too high a temperature and have killed the yeast.

COUNTING THE COLONIES

Laboratories that routinely perform this type of work, will have at their disposal an instrument known as a "colony counter". It consists essentially of a magnifying glass, a grid board and a light. Small brewers who do not perform this operation often can very well do the counting without resorting to this instrument, and still get accurate results. Set the plate on a piece of grid paper. Get adequate lighting and, if the colonies are small, a magnifying glass. Count the individual colonies in each square and add up the total.

For the number to be significant, 150 to 300 individual colonies should grow on the plate. If you have less than this you have diluted too much, and if you have more you have not diluted enough. In either case, you will have to redo the operation. The first time you perform this, you may not get it right. After a few times your eyes will get accustomed to the level of turbidity of the yeast dilution that gives the best results.

How many viable cells were present in the original suspension?

Once you have counted the individual colonies, backtrack to calculate how many individual cells were originally in the fermenting liquid.

Let's presume we count 175 colonies on the plate. If we started with a 10 ml solution that we diluted 4 times, this means that we had:

In one ml of the diluted solution in the no. 4 test tube: 175 cells, and in the whole test tube: 1750 cells.

17,500 cells in test tube no. 3

175,000 cells in test tube no. 2

1,750,000 cells in test tube no. 1

17,500,000 cells in the test tube that holds the original suspension.

COUNTING THE NUMBER OF YEAST CELLS IN A PITCHING STARTER

Using this method, you can count the number of live cells that you actually pitched in a batch of beer. Although this counting method is totally inadequate for a large commercial brewer or even a large microbrewer, it can still be recommended for smaller brewers. Its only drawback is that you get the actual result only when the beer has almost finished fermenting. However, this is the only way to know how many live yeast cells were present in your starter if you do not have a counting chamber and a microscope. The only materials required are petri dishes and nutrient agar. Whenever you meet with a problem of slow start or sluggish fermentation, this should be the first test you perform. By performing this test a few times, you will be able to refine the preparation of a good starter. Starter preparation will be dealt with later on (in the section on multiplying yeast in Chapter XV). Brewers who use this albeit slow method of evaluation a few times can improve their starter preparation and benefit from better fermentation.

Estimating the number beforehand

To get good results with this method, you must aim at having between 150 and 300 individual colonies on a plate. Assuming that we are using the dilution made in the preceding chapter, we can calculate the following:

1 ml of the third dilution (15,000 cells per ml) will yield 1,500 cells.

1 ml of the fourth dilution (1,500 cells per ml) will yield 150 cells.

1 ml of the fifth dilution (150 cells per ml) will yield 15 cells.

Thus if we prepare plates with the fourth dilution, we should expect to obtain between 150 and 300 cells.

AGAR COOLING

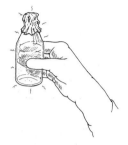

1. When the agar is completely liquefied, remove it from the boiling water and...

2. Place it in a cooling bath under running hot tap water.

3. Check the cooling bath temperature.

4. When the temperature has stabilized, gradually add cooling water.

5. Regularly check the cooling bath temperature. When it goes below 50°C, take the bottle and ...

6. Place it against your cheek. Hold it there for 5 seconds. It should feel comfortably warm. This is the correct temperature for pouring.

THE POUR PLATE METHOD

1. For this manipulation, prepare one or more empty sterile petri dishes...

2. A bottle or flask of liquefied nutrient agar...

3. A flame source...

4. A 1ml sterile pipette...

5. And a test tube holding 10 ml of the diluted yeast suspension. This will have been prepared ahead of time following the method outlined in Chapter x.

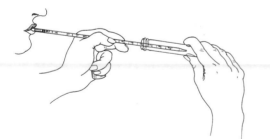

6. Using the method described in Chapter x, draw 1 ml of the diluted yeast suspension. Once the pipette is filled, adjust the volume to exactly 1 ml by releasing the pressure on your finger. When adjusted, keep your finger tightly on the tip.

7. Carefully lift the lid of the dish and move it sideways. Bring the pipette over the middle of the bottom portion of the dish. Lift your finger. The yeast suspension will flow into the dish.

8. Put the lid back on. Place the empty pipette in a suitable container. Do not place it on the work table. If you are doing more than one plate or dilution, do them now.

9. When completed, take the bottle of liquefied agar.

10. Double-check its temperature by placing it against your cheek.

11. Remove the aluminum foil protecting the opening.

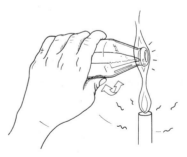

12. With your little finger, grasp the closure and immediately...

13. Place the flask opening in the flame. Keep the bottle closure in the palm of your right hand.

THE POUR PLATE METHOD

14. Lift the plate cover slightly and pour 15 to 20 ml of wort agar. The liquid should cover at least two thirds of the surface.

15. Put the lid back on, and give the plate a gentle twirl to evenly distribute and mix the yeast suspension with the agar. Five seconds is sufficient.

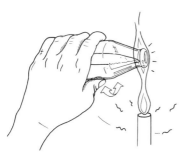

16. Between plates, keep the bottle opening in the flame. Proceed with the other plates.

17. If there is any wort agar left over, recap the bottle in a sterile manner.

18. After pouring, condensation will form on the cover. Do not move the plates until they have solidified. When solid, put a rubber band around the plates. Place them in a warm incubation area, with the media portion on top.

11.9

COUNTING THE CELLS

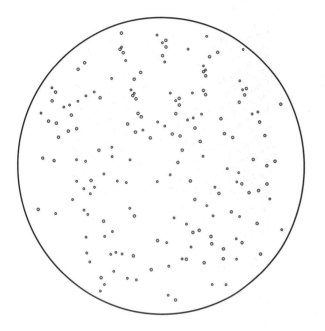

1. After five or six days the white specks of growing yeast are very evident. A well poured plate should give between 150 to 300 individual cells.

2. Place the plate over a sheet of paper lined with squares. Depending on the thickness and opacity of the nutrient agar, you may require back lighting.

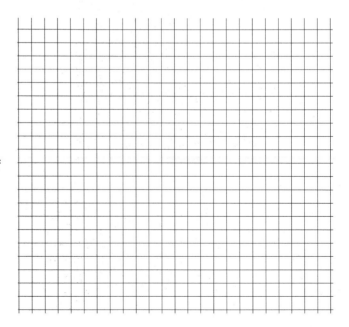

COUNTING THE CELLS

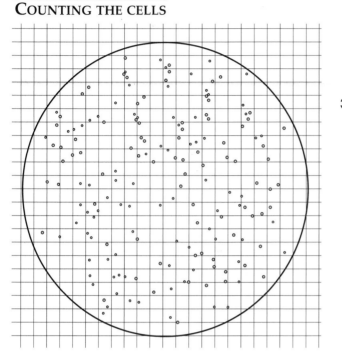

3. If needed, magnify the cells using a household magnifying glass. Starting at the left, count the number of cells in each column. If a cells touches or straddles a right grid line count it only once. Look carefully around the edges. A few cells will not be visible from the top, but will be from the side. Mark the side accordingly and add these cells to the total count.

4. Add the number of cells. Going back to the dilution factor, calculate the number of cells that were present in the original suspension.

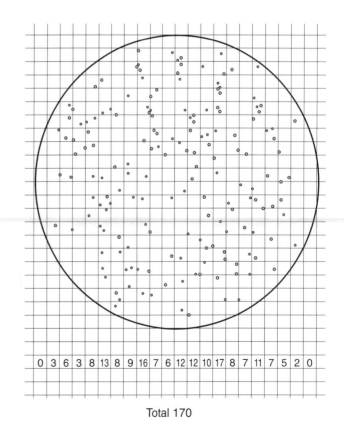

0	3	6	3	8	13	8	9	16	7	6	12	12	10	17	8	7	11	7	5	2	0

Total 170

TYPICAL PLATES: POUR PLATE METHOD

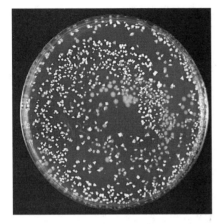

1. Plate poured over 1 ml of a 1/1000 dilution. This dilution held too many cells in suspension. Colonies are too close and numerous to be counted accurately. A count of this plate indicated 898 colonies. Anyone counting a plate such as this one would probably get within 10% of this number.

2. Plate poured over a 1/10,000 dilution. The number of colonies present on this plate totals 93. Half of the colonies are around the perimeter, but they are well spaced. See the picture further on for details of colonies around the edge of the plate. This density of colonies is good for accurate counting.

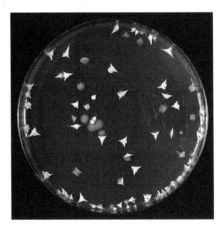

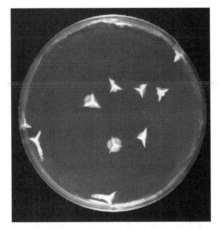

3. Plate poured over a 1/100,000 dilution. The colony count is too low for counting purposes. Only 9 colonies are present. However, they are well separated and have grown very well. These colonies are ideal candidates for saving on slants. The colony count on all plates reflects the dilution levels very closely.

Chapter XII: Cleaning glassware

One task that always confronts those engaged in yeast culture and microbiological work is the cleaning of glassware. Glass containers that have been submitted to the heat of the autoclave can at times be stubborn to clean. The same applies to glass vessels in which wort has fermented.

What cleaning agent is best?

Regular hand dishwashing detergent is quite inappropriate for this type of cleaning.

The most suitable and readily available detergent for this is domestic or institutional automatic dishwasher detergent. This detergent is efficient at high temperatures without scrubbing.

Tips on cleaning sterilized wort jars

Autoclaved glassware filled with wort and left standing for any length of time will accumulate a brownish film of particles on the sides and bottom. This will become quite apparent after emptying. Trying to remove this film with an ordinary hand dishwashing detergent is an impossible task. Even scrubbing with a brush will leave some residue.

Let the detergent do the work for you

To simplify the task, rinse the soiled glassware under hot running water. Bring some water to a boil. Sprinkle approximately ¼ tsp (1 g) of regular household automatic dishwasher detergent in the glass container. Fill the jar with boiling water right up to the brim. Notice the film on the sides literally fall apart and crumble. Let the flask sit like this for a few minutes. At the same time, place the closure separately in another container and treat it in the same way.

Shake vigorously

When the container has cooled down a bit, put the cap on and shake well. Pour the detergent solution out, rinse with hot water and inspect the container by looking through the glass at a lighted bulb. The glass should be spotlessly clean. Air dry and set aside. It is very important not to use a cloth to wipe it dry. Quite often it will grease the container.

Cleaning fermentation flasks and tubes

The same cleaning procedure should be used with glassware soiled by fermentation residues. Brewers who have access to industrial strength detergents will also find these very effective.

Before using the empty glassware, rinse with a brewery type sanitizer or household bleach to remove any dust that might have accumulated during storage.

REMOVING IDENTIFICATION MARKS AND RESIDUES

Glassware should always be properly identified, whether it is sterilized and empty or contains sterile wort. Any type of adhesive label can do the job. Some people prefer to use a wax pencil. I use pieces of masking tape. Whatever means you use is fine as long as it holds. However, markings and labels can sometimes leave stubborn residues. Acetone is effective in removing sticky residues and it is available everywhere. Simply wipe the surface of the glass with a paper towel wetted with a dab of acetone.

CHAPTER XIII: PRELIMINARY YEAST SELECTION

REMARKS ON INDIVIDUAL COLONIES

The purpose of plating a yeast is to obtain well separated colonies. By selecting individual colonies and keeping them, brewers aim at preserving the yeast in its original condition. Although this procedure seems simple, it is not so simple in reality. You can never be one hundred percent positive that a particular colony selected on a plate is composed exclusively of new cells originating from a single cell.

What can be wrong?

This was the principal conclusion that Hansen[1] made during his ground-breaking research on propagating yeast from a single cell. Hansen and Justus Chr. Holm,[2] a subsequent researcher, demonstrated that if you make a selection of one hundred well defined colonies on a series of plates, 8% of them originate from at least two or more cells. These two cells could be of the same strain or of different strains. The method Hansen used to arrive at this conclusion will be described in the second volume of this book.

This does not mean, however, that picking colonies from a plate is not reliable. It is still an excellent means of selecting and preserving yeast. If you select an individual colony from a plate, ferment it and plate it out again, you increase the chance that the new individual colonies on this second plate will be similar to each other.

A review of plating

Let's assume that you have inoculated a test tube with a freshly acquired yeast. As soon as it is actively fermenting, plate it out. You have the choice of either making two plates in succession (described in the section *How to obtain single colonies without diluting* in Chapter IX), or first diluting the yeast in sterile water and from that dilution making the plates. You will soon have large colonies growing. Colonies growing on a plate prepared by the pour plate method are also very good candidates for yeast selection. A poured plate having approximately twenty separate colonies is a very good starting point.

THE FIRST SELECTION

The first operation is to pick individual colony from the plate and inoculate each one separately in a different tube. When these tubes show signs of fermentation, make new slants for back-up purposes and put them away.

Meanwhile you will have fermented a beer with the original acquired yeast. If you are satisfied with the resulting beer, you can now further refine your culture. Reinoculate the slants previously saved, then make fresh new plates with them. If you selected 4 colonies from the first series of plate, there is a good chance that you will have a choice of more than 16 colonies on this second series of plates. At this stage, I take four or five individual colonies on the second series of plates, and inoculate them in the same tube. As soon as this tube is fermenting, I make slants. When I want to ferment again, I use the yeast from this new slant to prepare my starter. This has worked very well.

The preservation

In the second volume of this book, I will describe a series of tests and observations for evaluating colonies that show more merit than others. However, for the majority of brewers selecting and mixing individual colonies from this second series of plates will suffice. If the yeast used for making the first selection was of good origin, you have an excellent chance of success. Yeast acquired from a reputable supplier usually comes from a good selection. If you have fermented successfully with a specific yeast, you can safely assume that it is of good quality and fairly stable.

It is also very important to consider that we have not yet tested for the presence of wild yeasts or beer-damaging bacteria. Bacteria, wild yeasts or their spores could be present in the colony you select. The chances are extremely low, but the possibility exists. The second volume of this book will deal with the ways and means of detecting and identifying the most common wort and beer-damaging bacteria.

Multistrain yeast

The only case where saving individual colonies does not work is with multistrain yeast. You cannot be sure of its composition. I advise brewers to stay away from these yeast strains unless they have lots of time and patience. Even with a microscope you cannot pick out multistrain yeast. The shape, size and appearance of even a pure single cell culture varies.

The first step to a pure culture

Those who have the time and the desire can go one step further. Take an individual colony from the second series of plates and multiply it in the manner described in Chapter xv. Ferment a complete batch with it. If the result is satisfactory, you have made a good yeast culture. Although, practically speaking, it might behave and perform as well as a true pure culture, technically it should not be considered a true single cell yeast culture.

Bacteria

Plating a yeast suspension can also provide a test for the presence of aerobic bacteria. Wort bacteria are the kind that can grow on a plate made from hopped wort. However, they are noticeable only when they are quite numerous. Low levels can only be detected on plates prepared with a media that prevents the growth of yeast.

Beer-damaging bacteria such as the acid-forming lactobacillus and pediococcus also need special media to grow, and must be cultured in a CO_2 atmosphere. They will visibly grow only on a media that suppresses the growth of the yeast.

Pure yeast culture: a summary description

Propagating yeast from a single cell is the only way to be certain you are obtaining a pure yeast culture. Here is a summary description of the procedure:

The first requirement is a yeast that already ferments very well. A sample taken from the actual fermenting vessel is diluted in water and then further diluted in wort. A drop of the liquid is examined under the microscope. Each drop that is positively identified as containing only one yeast cell is allowed to ferment under sterile conditions. Each of these drops will produce a single cell pure yeast culture. Each of these pure cultures is then examined and tested. Some are selected and others discarded. Such a thorough investigation requires much competence and time. At this stage, you may begin to understand why the price demanded for a pure yeast is more than the price of a mass-produced one. This long and very precise manipulation will be fully described in the second volume.

REFERENCES

1. HANSEN EMIL CHR. *M. Carlsb. II 4th booklet, 152* (1886)

2. HOLM JUSTUS CHR. *Zeitschr. f. d. ges. Brauwesen N. 20* (1891)

TYPICAL PLATES: YEAST AND BACTERIA

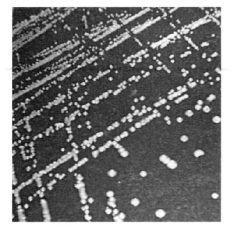

1. Plate streaked directly from wort fermented with the yeast of a bottle conditioned beer. The presence of numerous small colonies on this first plate makes it rather difficult to distinguish the yeast colonies from the bacteria colonies.

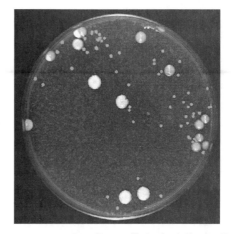

2. The same yeast culture diluted at the ratio of one loopful of yeast culture to 3 ml of sterile water. The yeast colonies are surrounded by wort bacteria colonies. On this second plate, fewer yeast colonies are present and they grow bigger. The bacteria colonies, much smaller, are now quite evident.

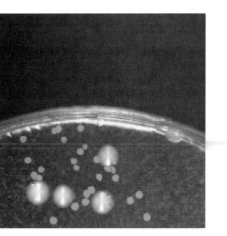

3. Close-up of another plate of the same diluted yeast culture. The yeast colonies are surrounded by wort bacteria colonies. The bacteria colonies are very close to the yeast colonies. It is safe to assume that some bacteria cells could be present under some yeast colonies.

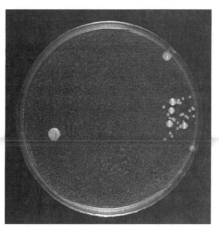

4. The big yeast colony at eight o'clock is well isolated. A culture started from that colony was bacteria free.

TYPICAL PLATES: YEAST AND BACTERIA

1. Close-up of yeast and wort bacteria colonies. Arrow indicates an indentation in the yeast colony. This is most likely caused by the presence of a bacteria colony growing in the same area that has been overcome by the stronger growing yeast cells. Do not reculture such colonies.

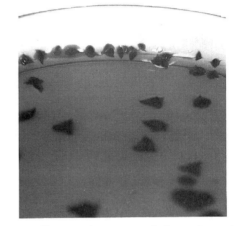

2. Yeast cells growing around the edge of a petri dish. This is very frequent when using the pour plate method.

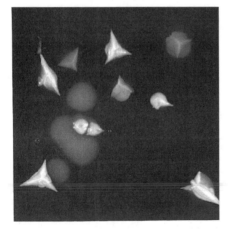

3. Individual colonies growing on a plate prepared with the pour plate method. Although the yeast colonies started to grow inside the agar they eventualy broke throught the surface and produced these triangular shaped outlines. The yeast cells deeper in the agar have kept their circular shape.

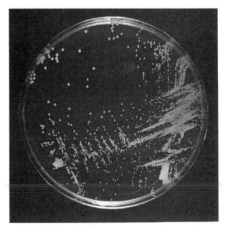

4. The same wort bacteria infected culture as shown on the photos on the previous page. The culture is plated on NBBA agar. This media prevents the growth of yeast and allows only the growth of bacteria.

Chapter XIV: Saving yeast in a sucrose solution

A complement to slants

The majority of brewers keep their yeast cultures on agar slants. This is excellent if you reculture every three months. There is, however, an almost forgotten way of preserving and maintaining yeast cultures. This method is more than a century old. It consists in preserving the yeast strain in a dormant state, by placing a small inoculum of cells in a 10% sucrose solution. This method is very efficient, and also has the advantage that anyone can do it with ingredients that are already present in the house. The only essential item required is a pressure cooker.

A conservation method poorly described

I started using this method because it gave me an extra backup for yeast preservation. I had been dubious about its value, because there was no explanation on how to do it. Although this method is summarily mentioned in brewing textbooks, very few authors provide practical details.[1] We find such short mention as: yeast can be kept in a 10% sucrose solution. Many sources have conflicting opinions on how to go about it. After searching many old,[2] and newer textbooks, I came across enough information to attempt it and finally adopt it. Following is the method that I use.

REQUIRED INGREDIENTS

Sugar

First prepare the sugar solution. A 10% percent sugar solution means you dissolve 10 g of sugar into 90 g of liquid. The sugar used for this purpose is just plain granulated sugar. The liquid can be tap or spring water. Weigh the water and dissolve the 10 g of sugar in it. You can also measure the 90 g of water as being 90 ml. Precision here is recommended, but not essential. Final adjustments will be made anyway.

Water

The water you use should be ordinary tap water or spring water. Do not use distilled water. All drinking water contains a variable quantity of trace minerals. The authors that have described this method recommend tap water. I have not been able to find any other specifications, so you should be the judge. The tap water used for brewing is also good for making the sucrose solution. Of course, I would either filter or boil it beforehand to remove the chlorine. If you like drinking your tap water, it's probably balanced. If you don't, purchase good spring water.

Adjusting the concentration

Once the sugar is diluted in the water, there is an easy way of double-checking the concentration: measure the specific gravity. Pour the solution in a hydrometer jar and take a reading. A 10% sugar solution has a reading of 10° Plato. A hydrometer graduated in only specific gravity must indicate 1.040 at 20°C, and one graduated in Balling degrees must read 9.925. Most hydrometer jars hold at least 200 ml of liquid, so prepare beforehand at least 200 ml of solution. If the reading is a bit off, you can either add sugar to increase it or water to decrease it. With precision in weighing few adjustments should be required.

Making the solution without a scale

You can also prepare a sucrose solution without a scale. One teaspoon of sugar weighs roughly 4 g. So measure two and a half teaspoons of sugar and add it to 90 ml of water. You will end up very close. Once diluted, measure the specific gravity of the solution and adjust as described above.

Preparing test tubes and making a reserve

Divide the sucrose solution into test tubes. Ten ml in each test tube is sufficient. Save the surplus in a larger jar. Sterilize both the tubes and the reserve jar in the pressure cooker for 15 minutes. The resulting solution will not shed any deposit and will look like water with a slight yellow tinge to it.

What tubes to use?

This is the point on which I have found the most disagreement. Some authors say that the tube should be closed shut, while others say they should allow contact with ambient air. The controversy originates in the fact that a sucrose solution evaporates with time.

WHAT HANSEN USED

Freudenreich flask

Originally, Freudenreich flasks were used for this purpose. A Freudenreich flask is a small glass jar with a capacity of approximately 10 to 20 ml of liquid. It measures roughly 3 cm in diameter and 10 cm in height. It is fitted on top with a hollow cap of ground glass. The cap ends in a tube with an interior diameter of 0.2 cm. To allow the sugar solution to be in contact with air, the tube is packed tightly with cotton wool. Eventually, evaporation occurs. Some authors recommend sealing this tube, while others advise the opposite.

Hansen modified the Freudenreich flask by adding a glass tube outlet on the side. The top opening was packed with cotton wool, and the side arm was packed with asbestos and sealed with wax. He could sterile transfer through this side tube to a larger jar. With time, this also led to evaporation of the solution. This method was abandoned for another reason. Since the glass cap made the flasks top-heavy, they could easily tip over. The cotton wool would then get soaked, and the culture had to be discarded. For long storage the top tube was sealed with wax.

Sealed ampoules

Hansen flask

Others have advocated the sealed ampoule as an alternative.[3] The sugar solution was sterilized in tall test tubes closed with a cotton wool plug. The yeast was then inoculated and allowed to multiply. The top of the tube was then heated over a flame until the glass melted, and the top portion of the tube was pulled to make a seal. The excess portion was cut off. The yeast sugar solution was thus completely sealed. This conservation method was very common a century ago. Chemists and laboratory personnel were quite proficient at heating glass to make sealed ampoules. Today, this method has dropped out of usage with the availability of quality test tubes with screw-on caps. The art of sealing a glass tube has been lost.

Test tubes taped shut

I have also tried keeping a sugar solution in a tube closed with polyplugs and taped shut. This has helped somewhat, although the solution has a tendency to evaporate even when sealed. I now use test tubes either capped with screw-on lids or closed with solid rubber closures. Once prepared, the sugar solution will keep virtually forever in screw-cap tubes.

HOW MUCH YEAST TO ADD

This is a point on which everyone agrees: as little as possible. I proceed as follows. The first thing to do is to get vigorous yeast. Take it from either a slant or whatever you might have, and inoculate it in a test tube filled with 10 ml of hopped wort. Let it ferment for a few days. Release the CO_2 occasionally and loosen up the yeast. With the

14.4

inoculating loop, take a loopful of the fermenting liquid, and place it in a sterile manner in the sugar tube. Flame sterilize the sugar tube and then close.

It will seem as if there is no yeast in there. Do not worry, as there is enough. Keep it at room temperature. After four or five days, expect to see either white specs or flakes on the sides of the tube, or a small white dot at the bottom. Twirl the tube around between your fingers. The translucent liquid becomes a little white at the bottom. This is an indication of success. No more yeast will be produced, and this is what you will keep.

STORING THE CULTURE

Once again, I have read contradictory comments on this. Some authors say to keep the sugar culture at a cool basement temperature and to not refrigerate it. Others advise to keep it in the refrigerator. Personally I keep mine in a cool basement. In winter the temperature goes down to about 4°C, and in summer it might go up to 21°C. I have kept yeast in this way for over three years. It has always been successfully brought back to life when needed. I would imagine that this depends entirely on where you live and what access you have to a cool temperature.

What happens to the yeast in this state

Very little has been written on this subject. Most authors agree on a few points: yeast in a pure sugar solution ferments very slowly and multiplies very little. A sugar solution holds no nutrients and very little oxygen. The yeast uses its reserves to barely multiply and ferment. This results in no mutation. Because there is very little yeast present, there is no overcrowding. The cells are surrounded by the liquid. Some of the yeast will autolyse and die. The release of the autolysis secretions will serve as nutrients for some remaining cells. They will then assume a dormant state. If you inoculate the tube with lots of yeast, you will probably invite failure. A crowding situation will create an unhealthy environment for the yeast.

Think of yourself as a yeast cell

Yeast, as a living thing, behaves more or less like a human. The first people that lived on this planet were not numerous. They had no sewer, no garbage collection, and yet lived from day to day without problem. The absence of overcrowding allowed these events to go on without inconvenience for centuries. Yet situation of poor waste management was later a source of disease when people became too numerous. Yeast in a sugar solution is not crowded. Not enough byproducts are produced by dying cells to create a problem. There is a state of equilibrium. The yeast is comfortable and simply goes to sleep.

BE ON THE LOOKOUT FOR EVAPORATION

Evaporation is a decrease of water, but not of sugar. This creates a denser solution, which results in a change of the osmotic pressure on the yeast cells. The change in pressure disturbs the yeast cells and causes their death. To prevent this from happening, mark the level of each tube as soon as it has cooled from the autoclave. This way, if the liquid evaporates you will have visual proof of it.

What if it evaporates?

Although I employ every possible means of preventing the solution from evaporating, I came across an incident that aroused my curiosity. I had placed yeast in a series of test tubes closed with polyplugs and taped tight. For some reason the seal must have been defective, because I noticed that in two of the tubes the level went down. I immediately reanimated the yeasts in wort, and then inoculated them in fresh sugar solution tubes. However, I kept the original evaporated tubes and resealed them. I left them on the shelf and forgot about them.

Nine months later, I came across the tubes again. They had evaporated even more, and had lost half of the sugar solution. I had been negligent in another respect, since the tubes had also been kept rather warm. They had been exposed in summer to a temperature above 30°C. I was curious to see if they were still alive. After loosening up the yeast, I took a loopful and placed it in 10 ml of sterile wort. After three days, one of them started to ferment. I took a sample and examined it under the microscope. The cells were in excellent condition. The other tube held less yeast in suspension than the first one. Although I tried twice, it did not come back to life.

REANIMATING THE YEAST

Of course, when you preserve yeast cells in this manner, you preserve very few cells. Many of them will die. A few will go into dormancy.

To reanimate them, loosen up the yeast from the bottom or the side walls of the tube. The liquid will acquire a whitish sheen. Using the loop, pick up a loopful and inoculate it in a 10 ml hopped wort test tube. Because the yeast solution is very diluted, you pick up very few cells. Do not expect activity before three to five days. Some very strong yeast strains start to ferment after three days. The majority need four days.

Using and preserving

Once the yeast starts to ferment, I transfer it to promote vigorous multiplication. I repeat this one or two times. Then I reinoculate a new sugar solution tube and put it away. At the same time, I also prepare fresh slants.

I find this is an excellent method of keeping yeast. If you are ever in a rush and forget to reinoculate your slants every three months, this provides another backup method. The extra time needed for the yeast to jump back to life is the major inconvenience.

Preparing for a brewing season

I do most of my personal brewing in winter. So in early fall I bring back from dormancy the strains I have stored away on sugar, and make fresh slants. I use the yeast from the slants when brewing. The yeast jumps back to life much more quickly from a slant. At the same time, I also inoculate fresh sugar tubes.

THE ORIGIN OF KEEPING YEAST IN SUGAR

This method of preservation has withstood the test of time. It was first proposed by Hansen in the Carlsberg laboratory.[4] In those days breweries closed in summer since it was too hot and there was no method of refrigeration. They had to keep the yeast alive without brewing. For centuries, yeast preservation had been a concern for brewers. Some kept it pressed almost dry. This pressed yeast was placed in buckets and lowered into a cool well. Others covered their yeast with sugar and kept it in a cooled cave. This is probably were Hansen first got his idea. He kept all his yeast in a sugar solution.

How long will the yeast keep?

The Carlsberg laboratory has been at the forefront of yeast research for quite some time. In 1935, the director of the physiology department was Øjvind Winge. Although not as well known in brewing circles as Hansen, he was nevertheless a researcher of the same caliber. He was the first one to make a controlled sexual yeast reproduction. He accomplished this feat by dissecting two different yeast cells and mating two of their spores.

Out of curiosity, he tried to reanimate old yeast cultures that had been stored in a 10% sucrose solution.[5] Some of these had been prepared by Hansen 47 years earlier. Others had been prepared by Hansen's successor, Albert Klöcker, and were up to 30 years old. Winge succeeded in reanimating 10% of the Hansen cultures and 25% of the Klöcker cultures. This proved the validity of the sucrose solution preservation method. It was also noted that both the Hansen and the Klöcker collections had not been kept in an ideal environment as far as light and temperature were concerned. They had been somewhat neglected over time.

What can go wrong

There are a few inconveniences with this method. First, the medium is a liquid. You must take special precaution to keep the tube in a vertical position at all times. If you drop it, you loose everything. Most important is to check on evaporation.

Although this method has fallen out of usage, probably due to these inconveniences, it is nevertheless a method of preservation that is still endorsed by modern yeast scientists.[6] This method of storage is used mostly in Europe. It is not often mentioned in North American literature.

REFERENCES

1. MASTER BREWERS ASSOCIATION OF THE AMERICAS, ed. *The Practical Brewer*, Madison WI, 1986.

2. HOLM, J. CHR. *"Ueber die Aufbewahrung der Hefe in Saccharoselösung"*, Centr. f. Bakt. u. Par. 2. Abt. II (1896)

3. J. VAN GHELUWE, M. GILISSEN, P. FRAEYS. *"La culture de la levure pure en brasserie"*, Fermentatio N° 5 (1952)

4. HANSEN EMIL CHR. *M. Carlsb., 3rd booklet* (1898)

5. WINGE Ø. *Compt. rend. Trav. Lab. Carlsberg, Serie physiol. 21, 51,* (1935)

6. A. JÄHRING UND W. SCHADE. *Mikrobiologie der Gärungs- und Getränke Industrie,* (1993)

Chapter XV: Putting it all together

After this review of the basic manipulations necessary for proper yeast handling, let's put all this information together in a practical way.

Where to get yeast?

Most brewers obtain their yeast cultures from either a yeast wholesaler or a laboratory specialized in brewing technology. The major difference between these sources is the certification of yeast quality.

Yeast from a professional brewing laboratory

Yeast laboratories that maintain pure yeast culture strains and deal with commercial brewers throughout the world go to great pains to ensure the quality of their products. They not only supply the yeast strains, but also work with their client brewers. They help them select a particular strain adapted to the type of beer that they brew. Some laboratories have more than one hundred years of experience behind them. Some of the yeasts they carry have been in their collections for an equal amount of time. The results of numerous tests and experiments on the usage of a particular strain are of precious help in guiding the brewer's choice. These yeasts are always cultured from a single cell.

How much should I pay?

Of course, quality has its price. Some laboratories charge up to four hundred dollars for a yeast culture that is ready to propagate. This is a lot more than the current price on the homebrew market. Such laboratories always certify their yeast to be a pure culture, that is, free of bacteria and wild yeasts. I firmly believe that if you are a commercial brewer this is definitely worth the price. It will certainly give the brewer peace of mind, which is not always the case with homebrewing yeast.

Yeast from a commercial homebrewing yeast wholesaler

This does not mean that the quality of yeast available through the wholesaler is inadequate. Most wholesalers go through strict quality control measures to produce a yeast package of excellent quality. This type of yeast is adequate for homebrewing and for small commercial brewers adequately trained in yeast maintenance.

HANDLING HOMEBREWING YEAST CULTURES

First let's look at what I consider the proper way to handle commercial homebrewing cultures. Professional laboratory yeast cultures are always accompanied by complete instructions for yeast propagation under sterile conditions. The procedure is almost indentical to the one we will describe. The major difference is how far the propagation reaches a larger volume under sterile conditions. How to propagate the yeast will be covered first.

THE AGE-OLD WAY OF MULTIPLYING YEAST

More than a century ago, Hansen described a procedure for propagating a yeast culture from a single cell. This procedure will be described in details in the second volume of this book. Since Hansen's time, the procedure for yeast multiplication has stayed more or less the same. The first step is the inoculation of a small quantity of sterile wort to get the yeast active. Then the fermenting wort is transferred in successive steps to a progressively larger container. Ideally, each sterile transfer is made to a container that holds three to four times more wort than the fermenting container.

The benefits of multiplication

This procedure has the following benefits. First, each successive transfer promotes the multiplication of many young active cells. Second, because the wort is sterile there is no danger of outside infection. Building a starter in this way always produces excellent fermentation. At first, the procedure might seem time-consuming. However, if the material is prepared ahead of time only a few minutes are required for each successive step. A suggested yeast preparation timetable is detailed further on. If you follow this simple agenda, you will have an active starter in prime condition on brewing day.

THE REQUIRED INGREDIENTS

I have been following this method of yeast multiplication for over ten years. Through experience, I now know exactly when to start to be ready on brewing day. I have propagated yeast in volumes large enough to ferment 10-hectoliter brews. Operating under a tight schedule, this multiplication was completed in five days. A pure yeast culture and sterile wort made from pale malt were the only ingredients required. I never had to use any so-called "yeast boosters" or accelerators.

How major brewers do it

As a matter of fact, all major professional brewing textbooks written in the past hundred years recommend this method. Nowadays, very large brewers have sophisticated pure yeast culture plants, where they can monitor yeast growth and add oxygen, when required. However, the basic laboratory technique is the same. The yeast culture apparatus uses regular wort from the brew house. The only difference here is that the wort is completely sterile.

The major cause of bad beer

The important consideration here is yeast multiplication. This is accomplished by transferring. By working with sterile wort you eliminate wort infections. I shudder to think what happens when I read on some yeast packages,*"Expect to see signs of fermentation within forty eight hours"*. I have witnessed beer dumping in many breweries. In all cases, this was caused by a wort infection brought about by a slow start. By meticulously following the manipulations described earlier and adapting them to your particular situation, you will never experience bad fermentation. However, the results always depend on the quality of the yeast.

Evaluating the yeast at this early stage

If the yeast you are using shows defective performance, you will be able to detect it at these transfer stages. Transferring the yeast to a series of larger vessels allows you to smell and even taste the beer left over after each pouring. If anything is wrong, you will know before brewing.

YEAST MULTIPLICATION FOR HOMEBREWERS

What to look for

Yeast from wholesalers is shipped to you either on a slant or in a pouch. It should have a production or expiry date written on it. Under normal conditions you can expect the yeast to be viable. However, I would not order yeast too much ahead of time. Since proper yeast handling requires time and concentrated effort, start to propagate only when you actually have the intention of fermenting with it.

Getting going

You should aim at getting the yeast culture fermenting as soon as possible after breaking the seal or opening the slant. First, we will deal with yeast in the pouch, since this has not been covered so far. Starting with a slant is covered further on.

YEAST IN A POUCH

Follow the manufacturer's instructions to activate the yeast. As soon as you notice signs of activity, prepare the work area. Try to perform this manipulation in a dust and draft-free environment. Clean the work table with rubbing alcohol. Some specialists recommend that you also wash your hands with rubbing alcohol.

Preliminary preparation

Before opening the pouch, take two simple precautions to ensure the best sanitary conditions. First, wipe the part of the pouch that you will cut open with rubbing alcohol, and let it dry. Second, wipe the scissors blades with rubbing alcohol and briefly flame the blades. The alcohol left on the blades will burn upon flaming.

The ingredients

Have handy a bottle containing approximately 70 ml to 150 ml of completely sterile wort. By completely sterile I mean that the wort and bottle have been sterilized in the autoclave. A good sized bottle is a recycled juice jar with a total capacity of 300 ml to 500 ml. I recommend using trub-free wort. Follow the method of your choice in the preparing of trub-free wort (as described in the section *How to get crystal clear sterile wort* in Chapter III).

Getting oxygen in the wort

When you are ready to transfer the yeast, shake the sterile wort bottle vigorously to get as much air as possible dissolved in the wort. Do this a few times. Let the foam subside, then crack open the lid. You should ear a popping sound. Lay the bottle aside.

The first transfer, step by step

- Light up the flame source.
- Wipe the bag or pouch with alcohol.
- Wipe the scissors blades, and flame them.
- Cut open the pouch close to the flame.
- Using your free hand, grasp the wort bottle.
- Using the hand holding the pouch, grasp the lid.

- Unscrew the bottle.
- Working near the flame, pour the contents of the pouch into the bottle.
- Recap the bottle and lay it aside.

PREPARE A YEAST SAMPLE

The majority of brewers will stop here. I go one step further. After I have put the bottle back on the table, I keep the open pouch in the zone of the flame. Using my free hand, I take the inoculating needle and flame it. As soon as it has cooled, I plunge it inside the pouch to pick a loopful of the remaining yeast, withdraw it from the pouch, and keep it in the zone of the flame. I then place the pouch back on the table and take a test tube containing 10 ml of wort. I open the tube, flame it, and put the drop of yeast inside. I then lay the tube back in its rack.

The benefits of taking a sample

This operation gives me the following benefits. First, I can check the yeast culture under the microscope. Second, the tube can serve as a yeast source for either making a slant or plating out the yeast. This lets me keep my yeast testing and saving separate from the fermentation process.

Fermentation in the starter and in the sample tube

When you have finished, place the yeast bottle and test tube in a warm environment. The yeast bottle should show signs of fermentation in approximately four hours. The tube will be slower, and anytime up to twenty-four hours is acceptable. The time depends on the quantity of yeast you picked up with the loop. We will come back to the yeast bottle and sample tube further on.

THE PROCEDURE WITH A YEAST SLANT

The procedure varies a bit with yeast shipped on a slant. I do not recommend that you inoculate the yeast from a slant in any more than 10 ml of sterile wort.

Yeast in plastic slants

The manipulation consists in simply taking yeast from the slant with the loop and transferring it in a sterile manner to a 10 ml test tube. You have to be very careful about the flaming. If the yeast is in a glass tube, this presents no problem, and you can flame it normally. If it is in a plastic tube, you have to be more careful. Work near the flame but do not flame directly. Every time I do this, I have to be extremely careful. For years I have been working with glass tubes, and flaming is second nature to me. Before opening a plastic tube, I have to concentrate very closely on keeping it out of the flame.

What can go wrong

Once you have transferred the yeast to the tube, it should show signs of activity within 24 hours. Sometimes it will happen sooner, but it should never take longer than this. Beginners have to be careful here to let the loop cool sufficiently before taking the yeast from the slant. If you see no signs of activity after 24 hours, you may have picked up the yeast with a hot loop. If in doubt, redo the operation.

Getting ready for the transfer

As soon as you see signs of fermentation, follow the procedure outlined earlier to release the CO_2 and loosen up the yeast. Now you are ready to transfer the yeast to a tube holding three or four times the amount of wort. This will be described later.

Inoculate fresh slants

Before doing the first transfer, I always take the time to make one or two new slants of the fresh growing yeast. This is the best time to do it. The yeast is actively fermenting, so it will grow vigorously on the slant. It is also a cheap insurance against mistakes. It is very frustrating to drop a test tube with a slant when it is the only one you have. Having a backup is essential. Once the slants are inoculated, keep them warm for two to three days. Always identify the slants with the date and either the name or number of the yeast strain. When the agar surface is visibly covered with new growing cells, place the slants in the refrigerator.

The life expectancy of a yeast slant

Some authors say that yeast will keep for a long time on a slant. This is true up to a point. However, I recommend that you reanimate the yeast every three months. Take it from the refrigerator, and inoculate a test tube filled with sterile wort. After twenty-four hours make two new fresh slants. Date them and carry out the same procedure every three months. This works very well, providing the original yeast was of pure quality. Using this procedure, I have been able to keep many yeast strains for more than five years. They still retain all of their original properties.

Yeast that does not keep well

Yeast made up of many strains is almost impossible to preserve this way, because you never know its exact composition. Multistrains are used in some breweries staffed with competent microbiologists and equipped with sophisticated monitoring apparatuses. They are encountered mostly in breweries in the U.K. Most breweries in the world use single strain yeast cultures. Personally, I have always stayed away from multistrain yeast. There are enough high quality single strains available. Small brewers who try to keep multistrains always end up with problems. Your supplier should be able to inform you as to the composition of the yeast.

Forgotten yeast

If you do not reinoculate the yeast every three months, anything can happen. Some strains will still be excellent after six months or even a year of storage on the same slants. Others will simply not come back to life again. Still others will produce different flavor or fermentation characteristics. Reinoculating every three months prevents disappointment.

The key to success

Wort infection is the greatest enemy you have to combat in yeast multiplication, and sterile wort is the key to success. Yeast from a reputable supplier should be bacteria and wild yeast-free.

THE FIRST TRANSFER

At this point, the new slants are made and the test tube is fermenting. Now, it is time to transfer. There is very little CO_2 present yet and getting all the yeast in suspension is easy (as described in the section *Start releasing the CO2*, in Chapter VI). After twelve hours of fermentation, the presence of CO_2 is greater and its release requires more time. Whatever time is required, do it properly.

Get the yeast in suspension

Most yeast make a compact deposit at the bottom of the tube. Make sure it is broken down and in suspension. Otherwise, the yeast clumps will fall back to the bottom of the tube, and might be left behind when transfering. However, you will still get some yeast transferred over to the new tube. The only inconvenience is that the renewal of fermentation will take more time. This can be frustrating when you are on a tight schedule. After transferring, you will have approximately 40 ml of fermenting wort.

Transfer again

As soon as signs of fermentation are quite visible, transfer this 40 ml quantity of wort again to a sterile juice jar holding approximately 120 ml of wort. Homebrewers should follow the procedure described in the section *getting oxygen in the wort*, in this Chapter. This will result in a quantity of approximately 160 ml of fermenting wort.

YEAST STARTER PREPARATION

1. Have ready a bottle containing approximately 100 ml of sterile wort.

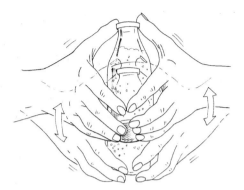

2. Shake vigorously to aerate thoroughly. Let the foam subside.

3. Wipe with alcohol the outside of the pouch and the sterile wort bottle.

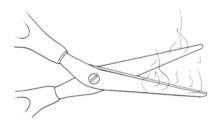

4. Also wipe the blades of a pair of scissors, and flame them briefly.

5. Cut the pouch. Open the wort bottle and pour the yeast inside. Do not cap tightly. Leave it cracked open to allow the CO_2 to escape.

6. Expect to see signs of fermentation within four hours. Then begin loosening up the yeast and prepare a transfer to a larger jar.

YEAST STARTER PREPARATION

7. Have ready a sterile jar of a one to two-liter capacity.

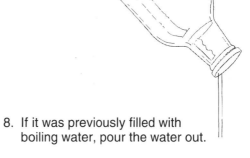

8. If it was previously filled with boiling water, pour the water out.

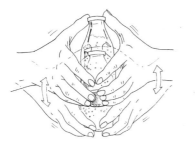

9. Aerate a bottle holding approximately 300 ml of sterile wort, shaking vigorously.

10. Open and flame briefly.

11. Pour the wort in the bottle and cap immediately.

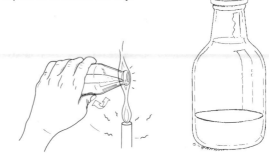

12. Open and lightly flame the yeast bottle. Open the wort jar and pour in the fermenting yeast, which has previously been loosened. Cap the wort jar immediately. If unable to check on it again within four hours, crack open the cap or replace it with a cap fitted with an air lock.

15.11

COMMERCIAL MULTIPLICATION

A commercial brewer should always transfer to sterile flasks with openings that can be flame sterilized. Multiplying yeast for the long term requires flasks and bottles that can be totally sterilized in the autoclave. Because these flasks do not have solid closures, it is impossible to aerate the wort by shaking. This may lead to a marginally slower multiplication rate. However, when transferring over to larger vessels you will have ample opportunity to splash the wort around for aeration purposes. With proper equipment, commercial brewers can even inject sterile air or oxygen into large fermenting vessels.

TRANSFERRING TO LARGER FLASKS

From now on, the manipulation is the same whether the yeast came from a pouch or from a slant. The next step is to transfer over to a larger jar. At this stage, variations in the procedure depend on whether the yeast is going to be used for home or commercial brewing. If you are a homebrewer and you intend to reuse the yeast, you can follow the next procedure in all safety.

Preparing larger jars

To transfer to a larger jar, you can select a jar that has been either completely sterilized in the autoclave or sterilized by the boiling water method. A two-liter jar is ideal, because it leaves enough space for several additions of wort. With a large pressure cooker you can sterilize jars of this size either empty or containing approximately 300 ml of wort. Although this step would be essential for commercial multiplication, it is not an absolute necessity for home brewing. The procedure for preparing sterile jars outlined below is completely adequate for this purpose.

Notes on preparing bottles by the boiling water method

Preparing the bottle

This method allows brewers who do not have a large enough pressure cooker to sterilize jars for either multiplying or saving yeast. I have used it with complete success for over ten years. It consists simply in filling an empty clean glass jar right up to the brim with boiling water. When the bottle is full, invert it to get the lid in contact with boiling water. Use well insulated gloves to do this. Leave upside down for approximately fifteen minutes. Then put it right side up again. After another fifteen minutes the bottle is ready for use.

Using the bottle

A bottle prepared in this way can be stored still filled with water. Just mark it accordingly. When it is needed, just pour the water out. Do not lay the lid on the table. Keep it in your hand, making sure that you hold the open lid face down when pouring. If you decide to use a bottle right after treating it with boiling water, wait until the bottle cools down before putting yeast in it.

The difference between autoclaved and boiled water bottles

The only difference between a bottle sterilized empty in the autoclave and one treated with boiling water is that the inside air of an autoclaved one is also sterile. For a boiled water bottle, when you pour the water out, the air that flows in is not sterile. The success you obtain with this method thus depends on the quality of the ambient air. However, the possibility of infection is minimal. When you use a bottle treated in this way for yeast multiplication, you are working with sterile wort anyway. If you use one for yeast storage, the result will be almost the same. You are placing in it a large quantity of yeast that will be reused shortly. (For illustrations on the preparation of boiled water sterilized bottle see the section on *Wort hot packing* in Chapter III).

Preparing the wort

If the large jar sterilized in the autoclave is already filled with 300 ml of sterile wort, simply pour in the contents of the smaller jar of fermenting wort. If the large jar was prepared by the boiling water method, it must first be filled with sterile wort. Take a bottle containing 300 ml to 400 ml of sterile wort, and shake it vigorously to aerate it thoroughly. Let the foam subside.

If the large jar is still filled with water, pour it out. For homebrewers, working with the flame is optional. As mentioned earlier when manipulating larger jars you may wish you had four hands. I personally feel that you can be as efficient by working quickly than by flaming awkwardly. Of course, all of this should be done under the ideal conditions of still air and no dust.

THE TRANSFER TO A LARGER JAR

Filling the jar with sterile wort

- Crack open the lid of the large jar.
- Crack open the lid of the small wort jar.
- Open the lid of the small wort jar and discard the lid.
- Quickly open the lid of the large jar, keeping it face down in the palm of your hand.
- Pour the wort from the small jar into the large jar, and close the large jar immediately.

This whole operation requires from four to five seconds.

A quick check on wort

If for any reason you doubt the quality of your sterile wort, now is the time to check it. After it has been transferred, smell the empty bottle. You will know immediately whether it is alright. Do this before adding the yeast. This would be absolutely necessary if, when using sterile wort from a recycled bottle, you did not hear a popping sound when you cracked open the cap. Although I personally have never had bad wort in such cases, this smelling procedure has become routine. Once, when multiplying a yeast from a bottle-conditioned beer, I forgot to do it. The sluggish performance of the yeast left me in doubt as to whether the origin of the problem was the yeast or the wort. The only solution was to discard everything. Since you have not yet poured in the yeast, if the wort is dubious the problem is easy to solve.

Filling the jar with fermenting wort

- Pick up the fermenting jar and give it one last twirl to get the yeast in suspension.
- Open the small fermenting jar and discard the lid.
- Open the large jar, following the same precautions outlined earlier.
- Pour the yeast inside the large jar, and close the lid.

Renewed fermentation

After four hours you should see signs of activity. After all these transfers, the total amount of wort in active fermentation should be from 450 to 600 ml.

Practice with water

If unsure about your ability, practice with water. After a few trials, you will be pleased to see how quickly the transfer can be done.

AN ADDITIONAL MULTIPLICATION

The next step is optional. You now have a fairly good starter. Some brewers will pitch it in the usual batch of 18 liters. I go one step further on brewing day. I add up to 500 ml of wort to the starter. When doubling up like that, expect to see signs of fermentation in just one hour. I always have on hand many topping up bottles, each holding roughly 400 ml of sterile wort. After doubling, I end up with over one liter of actively fermenting wort.

The advantage of large bottles

This is where it is beneficial to have done everything in a two-liter jar. After this last topping up, there should be as much headspace in the jar as there is liquid. There is one good reason for this. When you twirl the jar around to get all the yeast in suspension, the wort will foam. If the headspace is too small, you have to be very careful of gushing. You can twirl the jar, but you will have to take your time. The size of the jars that you can put through the autoclave or sterilize with boiling water is the deciding factor here.

A SUGGESTED TIMETABLE

The accompanying illustrations summarize these operations. You will notice that two timetables are suggested. One is for top fermenting "ale" yeast and the other for bottom fermenting "lager" yeast. Thus far, the procedure is the same whether the yeast is a top or bottom fermenter.

THE CASE OF BOTTOM FERMENTING YEAST

There is one major difference with bottom fermenting yeast. The propagation starts at room temperature. If you do all multiplications at room temperature and then add the starter to cold wort, this will shock the yeast. Many years ago I was unaware of this effect, and was shocking my yeast in this way. At times I would experience lags of two or three days before seeing the first signs of fermentation. The resulting beer always had a taste that was not quite the desired one.

The correct way of doing it

Since then, I have followed the method of multiplying bottom fermenting yeast that is used by the major brewers. They lower the fermentation temperature of a bottom fermenting yeast after each successive transfer. Of course, they do not often start a new yeast from scratch. But the seed yeast used in the yeast propagation system has gradually become accustomed to the fermentation temperature.

Do not rush the multiplication

Lowering the temperature at each step is not always feasible for a homebrewer or even a small commercial brewer. But all possible means of gradually bringing the yeast to a lower temperature should be considered. Although the timetable suggests transferring every twenty four hours, this may not always be possible. If you have lowered the temperature too much, the yeast might not yet be actively fermenting after this amount of time. You can wait another twenty four hours. However, completely acclimatizing the yeast at each step is essential for top quality. Until I started doing this, I was never completely satisfied with the overall flavor profile of bottom fermented beers. I was tempted to blame it on the yeast. I preferred the taste of top fermented beers, since their flavor seemed truer. Now I really obtain the desired richness and quality all the time with a bottom fermented beer.

Ready for fermentation

By following this approach, you now have a sufficient quantity of fresh yeast to ferment a normal 18-liter batch. After pitching one liter of active ale starter in 18 liters of wort, you will see signs of fermentation within twelve to eighteen hours. I consider this amount of time to be normal and adequate. However, if I intend to reuse the yeast for several brews, I go one step further in building up the yeast. If doing a bottom fermentation, this additional step is almost essential.

DOING ONE MORE BUILDUP

I transfer the one liter of starter into only four liters of wort. This, I admit, is quite tricky because somehow you have to keep the balance of the 18 liters that you have just brewed in cold storage. To simplify this, I ferment four liters in a smaller vessel, and keep the balance of the wort at a near freezing temperature in the vessel for fermenting the whole batch.

The way you do this depends entirely on the type and size of vessels at your disposal, as well as the facilities available to preserve unfermented wort.

The ideal small fermenter

I find fermenting in a smaller vessel very easy. Use a stainless steel stock pot with a capacity of approximately 10 liters. Most major discount stores and merchandise depots sell them cheaply. These pots are made of thin stainless steel, and may not be well suited for heavy duty work nor serious cooking, but make great small sized fermenters. They are easy to clean, and can also be dry heat sterilized in the oven.

Splitting the wort

Fill a sterilized pot with four liters of wort as soon as it comes out of the chiller. This is easily accomplished by having the lid cracked open. As soon as the right level is reached, put it aside and fill the full-size fermenting vessel with the balance of the wort. When this second vessel is filled, chill it immediately by putting it in an ice bath. Since it has been filled with chilled wort at 20°C, further chilling takes little time. Go back to the first vessel and pour the active starter in it right away. This four liters will show signs of activity within four hours. Depending on the time of the day you do this, you can either transfer it to the main fermenter soon afterward, or let it ferment overnight.

Warm up the reserve wort

Before adding this four-liter batch to the balance of the wort, warm up the unfermented wort to fermentation temperature. This additional buildup always results in excellent fermentation. With the addition of this four-liter starter, the entire 18 liters will be actively fermenting within three to four hours.

THE RESULT IS WORTH THE EFFORT

The resulting beer will taste like it should, and you will obtain an excellent crop of quality yeast that can be reused at least half a dozen times. The lag phase before the start of fermentation is reduced to a minimum. Keeping the unfermented wort cold prevents activation of any wort bacteria that might have been picked up. The risk of alteration is reduced to almost zero. At first glance, this procedure might seem like a lot of work, but if you intend to reuse the yeast for another batch, it is truly worth the effort.

The benefit of brewing in a cold climate

Some people will find this procedure easier to do than others. If you live in an area that is warm most of the year, it is definitely trickier to do. However, in a cooler climate it is easy, since the wort can be stored overnight outside or in an unheated garage at a temperature just above freezing.

ANOTHER APPROACH

There is another way to achieve the same result. Instead of making one starter, make two. Just double the number of tubes and flasks at each step. It does not take more time to prepare a double amount of starter. Every time I propagate yeast in commercial quantities, I do it this way. The largest jar that I can sterilize has a useful capacity of two liters. The next larger vessel I use is a fermenter with a twenty-five liter capacity. This fermenter is filled hot with twenty liters of brewery wort. Once cooled, I inoculate it with two active starters of two liters each, resulting in a further fourfold increase.

The method you use should suit your needs

The number of yeast transfers you make depends entirely on what you need. If you are going to ferment only one brew, and discard the remaining yeast, you definitely do not need to do all these transfers.

If you are multiplying a bottom fermenting yeast, however, these last multiplication steps will be absolutely necessary. First, you have another opportunity to lower the temperature. Second, the yeast will go through a further multiplying step. Pitching just one liter of starter in 17 liters of wort will usually lead to a lag time of forty-eight hours. The resulting beer will probably not have the desired richness of taste.

The addition of all this sterile wort will change my recipe

For some people, following an exact and strict recipe is very important. They may claim that adding extra amount of sterile wort at different stages will not give them the required taste or color. There is a bit of truth in this, but there is also another truth. If you really want to fine-tune a recipe, you need a yeast that is in top shape and in sufficient amounts. You have to make the choice. Either you neglect the yeast or you apply the recipe a little less rigidly. The aim of building a good starter to obtain a good yeast crop is not to get the best first batch, but rather to obtain great beer in the following fermentations.

Whenever major commercial brewers propagate a new yeast culture, they always put their first batch into storage. Under all circumstances they will blend it. As a matter of fact, their performance in the art of blending is of paramount importance in their market success.

Although this could be discussed at great length, I nevertheless find these first batches to be excellent on their own.

It's easy when you are prepared

If you have prepared yourself accordingly, each of these steps will require just a few minutes each day. You will be amply rewarded for your efforts.

YEAST MULTIPLICATION: TOP FERMENTATION

Brewing day minus three: at night

1. Pick a loopful of yeast from a slant, and inoculate a 10 ml test tube.

Brewing day minus two: at night

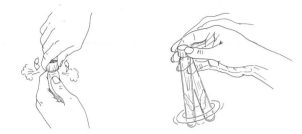

2. Fermentation signs will develop within 24 hours. Release the CO_2 and get the yeast in suspension.

Brewing day minus two: at night

3. Transfer the 10 ml of fermenting wort from the small test tube to a larger tube containing 30 ml of sterile wort.

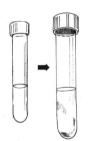

Brewing day minus one: in the morning

4. Transfer the 40 ml of fermenting wort into a jar holding approximately 100 ml of well aerated sterile wort.

Brewing day minus one: at night

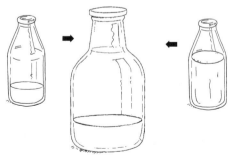

5. Transfer the 150 ml of fermenting wort to a larger sterile jar. Add 300 ml of sterile wort.

Brewing day: in the morning

6. Add another 300 ml of well aerated sterile wort.

Yeast multiplication: bottom fermentation

Brewing day minus six: at night

1. Pick a loopful of yeast from a slant, and inoculate a 10 ml test tube. Allow the yeast to multiply at 21°C.

Brewing day minus five: at night

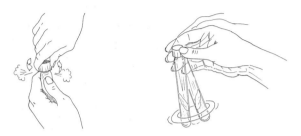

2. Fermentation signs will develop within 24 hours. Release the CO_2 and get the yeast in suspension.

Brewing day minus five: at night

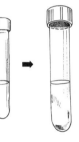

3. Transfer the 10 ml of fermenting wort from the small test tube to a larger tube containing 30 ml of sterile wort. Lower the temperature from 21°C to 19°C.

Brewing day minus four: at night

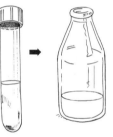

4. Transfer the 40 ml of fermenting wort into a sterile jar holding approximately 100 ml of well aerated sterile wort. Lower the temperature from 19°C to 17 °C.

Brewing day minus three: at night

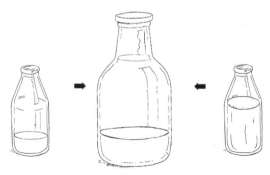

5. Transfer the 150 ml of fermenting wort to a larger sterile jar. Add 300 ml of sterile wort. Lower the temperature from 17°C to 15°C.

Brewing day minus two: at night

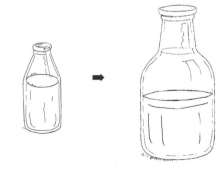

6. Add 300 ml of sterile wort. Lower the temperature from 15°C to 13°C. Allow to ferment up to brewing day. Then add another 300 ml of well aerated sterile wort. Lower the temperature to 11°C.

15.22

Chapter XVI: **Saving yeast**

If you have multiplied yeast following the recommended procedures, you have been rewarded with an excellent fermentation. We now come to the important manipulation of collecting and saving the yeast for future fermentation. The general collecting procedure is simple. Small variations may be required to suit the container used for fermenting.

Equipment needed

- Sterile containers or jars
- A suitable funnel
- A hooked piece of wire to grab the funnel
- A pot deep enough to cover all utensils with boiling water
- A long-handled stainless steel spoon (optional)
- A cap fitted with an air lock to close the yeast jar
- A small bottle holding approximately 300 ml of sterile water

The need for sterile equipment

Have the jars prepared ahead of time. They must be sterile. Sterilize them either in the autoclave or using the boiling water method, (as described in the section *The preparation of bottles by the boiling water method* in Chapter xv).

All the tools that will come in contact with the yeast must be washed beforehand, and then sanitized using an appropriate method. One such method consists in placing all the tools in a pan of boiling water.

I leave them there for ten minutes. This way, no final rinse is necessary. Boiled water does not contain any beer-damaging bacteria.

Of course, commercial brewers will not be able to use the boiling water method. Their vessels are much larger, and so is the quantity of yeast. Instead, they place all the necessary tools in a sanitizing solution. The yeast gathering vessel is also soaked with a sanitizer. Some brewers rinse the sanitizer from their tools before usage, whereas others use them as is.

TECHNIQUES FOR HOMEBREWERS

The following method applies to homebrewers. The methods and tools used in commercial brewing will be covered in the second volume of this book.

Loosening up the yeast

After primary fermentation is over and the major portion of the yeast has settled, the beer must be removed from the yeast. Some brewers siphon the beer, others let it flow out by gravity. In most cases, a small amount of beer will be left behind with the yeast. As soon as the transfer is completed, swirl the vessel around to get the yeast suspended in the remaining beer. If not enough beer has been left behind and the yeast deposit is very compact, add 300 ml of sterile water. This will get the most stubborn yeast in suspension. With an open fermenter, use a long-handled spoon to loosen the yeast.

Preparing the transfer

As soon as all the yeast is in suspension, prepare to transfer. If you have prepared a jar using the boiling water method, discard the water and recap the jar immediately. If the jar is still hot, wait for it to cool down. Once cooled, remove the cap from the jar and place it in the boiling water. Using the hook, grab the funnel and place it over the mouth opening.

The best kind of funnel to use for yeast transfer is a widemouthed funnel. It lets the thick yeast flow in much faster. Canning funnels are quite suitable. Finding jars with large openings may be more difficult. For filling smaller mouthed jars, I use a so-called "powder funnel". This type of funnel is sold by laboratory equipment suppliers. It has an opening of about 20 mm. Yeast flows reasonably fast through it. If the yeast is very liquid, you can pour it directly into the collecting jar without using a funnel.

THE ACTUAL TRANSFER

With the funnel in place, pour in the yeast. This will require about twenty seconds. When enough has been collected, remove the funnel and recap the jar. I must add a necessary word of caution. **Do not leave a solid cap on the jar.** In many cases brewers separate the beer from the yeast when fermentation is not quite completed. Leaving a large amount of yeast in a small quantity of beer can cause a vigorous fermentation in a very short time. A tightly capped jar could explode under such circumstances, and cause bodily harm. As soon as possible after the transfer, replace the solid cap with one that is fitted with an air lock.

Air lock fitted caps

You cannot completely sterilize caps fitted with an air lock. The plastic used in manufacturing air locks distorts at the temperature of boiling water. However, an air lock fitted cap can be soaked in bleach and rinsed. The cap itself and the rubber are resistant to boiling water. Mount the air lock onto a previously drilled cap that fits the jar. Place the cap in a boiling water bath for a few minutes. Do not get the plastic from the air lock in contact with the boiling water. Now switch the caps, and place the yeast jar in the refrigerator. Make sure beforehand that the air lock mounted jar fits inside the refrigerator.

How long can the yeast be kept?

As a rule, I try to use this yeast within two weeks. It will be very vigorous. I do not advise keeping it longer. After a two-week period, yeast starts to autolyse. This results in the release of intracellular liquid, which leaves a harsh, bitter aftertaste.

SAVING LIVE BREWER'S YEAST

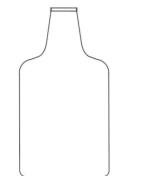

1. Have a clean and sanitized jar ready. Warm it up using hot tap water.

2. Discard the hot water and fill the jar right to the top with boiling water. Cap and invert it to sterilize the neck and the cap. Leave it like this for at least fifteen minutes.

3. Have handy a small bottle holding approximately 300 ml of sterile water to dilute the thick bottom yeast. Use it if required.

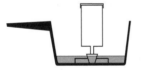

4. Prepare ahead of time a cap that fits the jar, and fit it with an air lock. Place it in a small pan partially filled with boiling water. Do not immerse the top plastic part in the water.

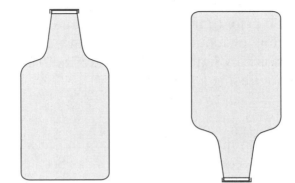

5. Fill a pan with boiling water. Place in it a long-handled spoon, a funnel and a hooked wire rod.

6. Transfer the beer from whatever fermenting vessel you used, leaving the yeast at the bottom. Loosen the yeast. In an open fermenter, you can use the sterile spoon. In a closed fermenter, add approximately 300 ml of sterile water if the yeast is too thick.

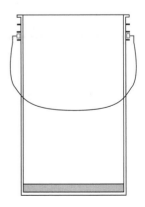

SAVING LIVE BREWER'S YEAST

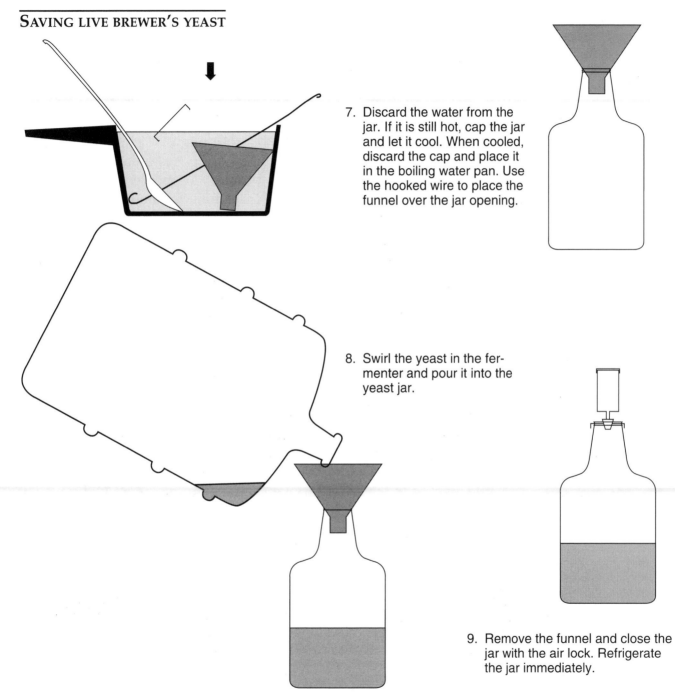

7. Discard the water from the jar. If it is still hot, cap the jar and let it cool. When cooled, discard the cap and place it in the boiling water pan. Use the hooked wire to place the funnel over the jar opening.

8. Swirl the yeast in the fermenter and pour it into the yeast jar.

9. Remove the funnel and close the jar with the air lock. Refrigerate the jar immediately.

16. 5

TRADITIONAL TOP FERMENTING STRAIN

The method of yeast collecting I have just described works very well with yeast that settles down quickly. In this class, we can include bottom fermenting strains and bottom settling top fermenting strains. Some ale yeast, however, mounts to the surface of the beer. If you are using such a strain in a closed fermenter fitted with a blowby tube, many of the new cells will be blown out through the tube. The yeast that deposits at the bottom will often be composed of inferior cells. When using such a strain, it is better to use a fermenter that permits collecting the top yeast. Follow the procedure outlined for collecting the bottom yeast, with one difference. Collect the yeast before transferring the beer to the aging vessel. Use the long-handled spoon to skim the yeast from the top. Place the yeast in the funnel you have mounted over the jar opening. This can be done as quickly as collecting from the bottom.

SAVING THE YEAST FROM SECONDARY FERMENTATION

Many brewers save the yeast slurry from the bottom of their secondary fermenter. They say that this yeast is cleaner and contains no residues. This might be true for the residues, but there is another danger. If by chance there are any bacteria or wild yeasts present in the primary fermentation, they will automatically be transferred to the secondary or aging tank. Bacteria are much lighter than yeast, and stay in suspension longer. Wild yeasts are mostly powdery strains, and do not settle quickly. In the secondary vessel there is almost no CO_2 buoyancy to keep the light particles in suspension. So the wild yeasts and bacteria settle. Although their effect may be negligible in a first brew, they can multiply drastically in subsequent ones. Collecting yeast from the secondary fermentation is an excellent way to increase the count. Saving and reusing this type of yeast should never be done.

CONVERSION CHART OF METRIC AND U.S. UNITS

Temperature

C°	F°
4°	39°
11°	52°
13°	55°
15°	59°
17°	63°
19°	66°
20°	68°
21°	70°
22°	72°
30°	86°
37°	99°
40°	104°
45°	113°
50°	122°
60°	140°
70°	158°
75°	167°
90°	194°
95°	203°
100°	212°
115°	236°
121°	250°
150°	302°
160°	320°
170°	338°
175°	347°
180°	356°
190°	374°

Volume

ml	U.S. fl oz
1	0.034
2	0.068
3	0.102
9	0.306
10	0.340
15	0.510
20	0.680
30	1.02
40	1.36
50	1.70
100	3.4
120	4.08
160	5.44
300	10.20
450	15.30
500	17.00
600	20.4

Volume

liter	U.S. gal
2	0.52
4	1.05
10	2.64
17	4.5
18	4.75
20	5.28
25	6.6

Volume

hectoliter	U.S. barrel
10	8.5

Volume

hectoliter	U.S. gal
10	264

Length

mm	inch
3	0.117
15	0.585
20	0.786
70	2.73
100	3.93

Length

cm	inch
0.2	0.786
3	1.17
4	1.56

Weight

gram	ounce
0.5	0.0175
1.2	0.0423
4	0.140
90	3.16
100	3.52

MARQUIS

Marquis Book Printing Inc.

Québec, Canada
2010